Merle Jones

KEEP IT CRISP

Other Books by

S. J. PERELMAN

DAWN GINSBERGH'S REVENGE

PARLOR, BEDLAM AND BATH
(*with Quentin Reynolds*)

STRICTLY FROM HUNGER

LOOK WHO'S TALKING!

THE DREAM DEPARTMENT

CRAZY LIKE A FOX

KEEP IT CRISP

by S. J. PERELMAN

RANDOM HOUSE   NEW YORK

FIRST PRINTING

Acknowledgements are due *The New Yorker*, in
which most of these stories first appeared, and to
The Saturday Evening Post for those stories
which were originally published in its pages.

TO MOTHER

CONTENTS

vii

KEEP IT CRISP

HELL IN THE
GABARDINES

AN OLD subscriber of the *New Republic* am I,
prudent, meditative, rigidly impartial. I am the
man who reads those six-part exposés of the South-
ern utilities empire, savoring each dark peculation.
Weekly I stroll the *couloirs* of the House and
Senate with T.R.B., aghast at legislative folly.
Every now and again I take issue in the corre-
spondence pages with Kenneth Burke or Malcolm
Cowley over a knotty point of aesthetics; my
barbed and graceful letters counsel them to reread
their Benedetto Croce. Tanned by two delightful
weeks at lovely Camp Nitgedaiget, I learn
twenty-nine languages by Linguaphone, sublet
charming three-room apartments with gardens

from May to October, send my children to the Ethical Culture School. Of an evening you can find me in a secluded corner of the White Turkey Town House, chuckling at Stark Young's review of the *Medea*. I smoke a pipe more frequently than not, sucking the match flame into the bowl with thoughtful little puffs.

Of all the specialists on that excellent journal of opinion, however, my favorite is Manny Farber, its motion-picture critic. Mr. Farber is a man zealous and incorruptible, a relentless foe of stereotypes, and an extremely subtle scholiast. If sufficiently aroused, he is likely to quote *The Cabinet of Dr. Caligari* four or five times in a single article (Mr. James Agee of the *Nation*, otherwise quite as profound, can quote it only once). It has been suggested by some that Mr. Farber's prose style is labyrinthine; they fidget as he picks up a complex sentence full of interlocking clauses and sends it rumbling down the alley. I do not share this view. With men who know rococo best, it's Farber two to one. Lulled by his Wagnerian rhythms, I snooze in my armchair, confident that the *mystique* of the talking picture is in capable hands.

4

It was in his most portentous vein that Mr. Farber recently sat himself down to chart the possibilities of the concealed camera. In transferring *The Lost Weekend* to the screen, you will recall, the producers sought verisimilitude by bringing Ray Milland to Third Avenue (in the past Third Avenue had always been brought to Ray Milland) and photographing the reactions of everyday citizens to Don Birnam's torment. The necessary equipment was hidden in theatre marquees, "L" stations, and vans along the route of the historic trek, and almost nobody knew that the scenes were being registered on film. Mr. Farber heartily approved this technique and called on Hollywood to employ it more generally. To demonstrate its potentialities, he even sketched a wee scenario. "If," said he, "your plot called for some action inside of a department store, the normal activity of the store could be got by sending trained actors into it to carry on a planned business with an actor-clerk. Nobody else in the store need become conscious or self-conscious of this business, since the cameraman has been slyly concealed inside an ingeniously made store dummy and is recording everything from there."

5

Through a source I am not at liberty to reveal without violating medical confidence, I have come into possession of a diary which affords an interesting comment on Mr. Farber's idea. It was kept by one Leonard Flemister, formerly a clerk in the men's clothing section of Wanamaker's. I was not a customer of Flemister's, as I get my suits at a thrift shop named Sam's on the Bowery, but I had a nodding acquaintance with him; we often occupied adjoining tables at the Jumble Shop, and I remember him as a gentle, introspective man absorbed in the *New Republic* over his pecan waffle. He is at present living in seclusion (the Bonnie Brae is not a booby hatch in the old-fashioned sense) in New Jersey. I append several extracts from his diary:

JANUARY 12—Today rounds out seventeen years since I started in the men's shop at Wanamaker's, and they have been years filled with quiet satisfaction. As our great Founder constantly observed in his maxims, it is the small things that count. How truly this applies to ready-made suits! To the tyro, of course, one suit is very much like an-

6

other, but to us who know, there is as much distinction between a Kuppenheimer and a Society Brand as there is between a Breughel and a Vermeer. Crusty old Thomas Carlyle knew it when he wrote *Sartor Resartus.* (Good notion, that; might pay me to have a couple of his quotations on the tip of my tongue for some of our older customers.)

Ran into Frank Portnoy yesterday at lunch; haven't seen him since he left us for Finchley's. Sound enough chap on cheviots, is Frank, but I wouldn't care to entrust him with a saxony or tweeds. He seems to have put on five or six pounds in the seat, and I thought his 22-ounce basket-weave a touch on the vulgar side. "Still working in that humdrum old place?" he asked, with a faint sneer. I kept my temper, merely remarking that he had incurred some criticism for leaving his position after only twelve years. (I did not bother to say that Mr. Witherspoon had referred to him as a grasshopper.) "Oh," he said airily, "I guess I learned enough of those lousy maxims." I said pointedly that he apparently had not learned the one about patience, and quoted it. He

7

termed it "hogwash." "Maybe it is," I retorted, "but don't you wish you could wash a hog like that?" He turned as red as a beet and finished his meal in silence.

Read a disturbing article in the *New Republic* last night. A man named Farber advocates secreting cameramen inside clothing dummies in department stores so that the clerks may unwittingly become actors in a movie. Of course it was just a joke, but frankly, I thought it in rather poor taste.

JANUARY 14—Felt a trifle seedy today; I must find some other lunch spot besides the Green Unicorn. Their orange-and-pimento curry appears to have affected my digestion, or possibly I have had a surfeit of banana whip. In any case, during the afternoon I experienced the most extraordinary sensation, one that upset me considerably. At the rear of our sportswear section, next to the seersucker lounging robes, is a perfectly prosaic wax mannequin wearing a powder-blue ski jacket, canary-colored slacks, and synthetic elk-skin loafers. About three o'clock I was hurrying past it with an armful of corduroy windbreakers when I heard a resounding sneeze. I turned abruptly, at first supposing it had come from a customer or salesperson, but the only one in sight was Sauerwein, who was absorbed in his booklet of maxims a good thirty feet away. Ridiculous as it may sound, the noise—a very distinct "Harooch!"— seemed to have emanated from the model. A moment's reflection would have told me that my auditory nerve was rebuking me for overindulgence at table, but unfortunately, in the first access of panic, I backed into a fishing-rod display and hooked a sinker in my trousers. Mr. Witherspoon, chancing by, observed (I thought with some coarseness) that I ought to get the lead out of my pants. Sauerwein, who loves to play the toady, laughed uproariously. I shall be on my guard with Sauerwein in future; I do not think he is quite sincere.

Saw a tiptop revival of *The Cabinet of Dr. Caligari* and *Potemkin* last night at the Fifth Avenue Playhouse; they are having their annual film festival. Enjoyed them both, though most of *Caligari* was run upside down and *Potemkin* broke in three places, necessitating a short wait. Next week they are beginning their annual *Potemkin* festival,

9

to be followed by a revival of *The Cabinet of Dr. Caligari*. Always something unusual at the Fifth Avenue.

JANUARY 17—Mr. Witherspoon is a tyrant on occasion, but as the Founder says so pungently, give the devil his due; every so often the quality that made him floorwalker shines through. This morning, for example, a customer I recall seeing at some restaurant (the Jumble Shop, I believe) created a scene. He was a peppery little gnome named, I think, Pevelman or Pedelman, with shaggy eyebrows and the tonsure of a Franciscan father. I noticed him fidgeting around the low-priced shorts for a half hour or more, trying to attract a salesman, but Sauerwein was behind on his maxims and I was busy rearranging the windbreakers. At length he strode over to Mr. Witherspoon, scarlet with rage, and demanded, in an absurd falsetto, whether he might be waited on. Mr. Witherspoon was magnificent. He surveyed Pevelman up and down and snapped, "Don't you know there's a peace on?" The customer's face turned ashen and he withdrew, clawing at his collar. Old Witherspoon was in rare good humor all morning.

10

Slight dizzy spell this afternoon, nothing of consequence. I wonder if anything could be amiss with my hearing. Curiously enough, it is normal except in the immediate vicinity of the mannequin, where I hear a faint, sustained clicking as though some mechanism were grinding away. Coupled with this is the inescapable conviction that my every move is somehow being observed. Several times I stole up on the dummy, hoping to prove to myself that the clicking came from within, but it ceased instanter. Could I have contracted some mysterious tropical disease from handling too many vicuña coats?

Sauerwein is watching me. He suspects all is not well.

JANUARY 20—Something is definitely wrong with me. It has nothing to do with my stomach. I have gone mad. My stomach has driven me mad.

Whatever happens, I must not lose my head and blame my stomach. A stomach blamed is a stomach spurned, as the Founder says. The only good Founder is a dead Founder. Or Flounder. Now I *know* I am mad, writing that way about the Flounder.

I must marshal my thoughts very carefully, try

11

to remember what happened. Shortly after one, I was alone in the department, Sauerwein and Witherspoon being at lunch. I was folding boys' windbreakers at the folded boys' windbreaker counter when a customer approached me. Never having seen Fredric March in person, I cannot assert dogmatically that it was he, but the resemblance was startling. From the outset, his behavior impressed me as erratic. He first struck a pose about fifteen feet from the mannequin, taking care to keep his profile to it. As he did so, the clicking sound which had harassed me became doubly magnified. Then, in the loud, artificial tone of one who wished to be overheard, he demanded to be shown a suit with two pairs of pants.

"We haven't any," I replied. "Don't you know there's a peace on?" To my surprise, he emitted a hoarse cry of delight and slapped his thigh.

"That'll be a wow!" he chortled. "We'll leave that line in!" Seventeen years of dealing with eccentrics have taught me the wisdom of humoring them; I pretended not to have heard. He gave me an intimate wink, snatched a sharkskin suit from the rack, and vanished into a dressing room.

12

I was on the point of summoning aid when he reappeared feverishly. The effect of the trousers, at least three sizes too large for him, was so ludicrous that I stood speechless.

"Just what I wanted," he grinned, surveying himself in the mirror. Simultaneously, almost as if by prearrangement, a young lady in flamboyant theatrical make-up appeared. To my horror, the customer forgot to hold onto his trousers and they dropped down around his ankles. "Hello, Vivian!" he cried. "Well, I guess you caught me with my pants down!" And then—I am resolved to spare no detail—a voice from within the mannequin boomed "*Cut!*"

When I recovered consciousness in the dispensary, the nurse and Mr. Witherspoon were chafing my wrists and Sauerwein was whispering to a store detective. I seem to remember striking Sauerwein, though I also have the impression my hands were entangled in my sleeves. The rest I prefer to forget. It can be summed up in the word "nightmare." Nightmare.

FEBRUARY 5—It is very quiet here at Bonnie Brae and the food is excellent, if a little unrelieved.

13

I could do with one of those tasty water-cress-and-palmetto salads they know so well how to prepare at the Green Unicorn. The library here is well stocked with current magazines; I keep abreast of the news via the *New Republic*, though I confess Farber does not grip me as he used to.

I have only one objection to this place. In the library is a suit of medieval armor, and very often I could swear that a pair of eyes are watching me through the casque. As soon as the weather becomes warmer, I expect to spend most of my time on the piazza.

FAREWELL, MY LOVELY
APPETIZER

Add Smorgasbits to your ought-to-know department, the newest of the three Betty Lee products. What in the world! Just small mouth-size pieces of herring and of pinkish tones. We crossed our heart and promised not to tell the secret of their tinting.—*Clementine Paddleford's food column in the Herald Tribune.*

The "Hush-Hush" Blouse. We're very hush-hush about his name, but the celebrated shirtmaker who did it for us is famous on two continents for blouses with details like those deep yoke folds, the wonderful shoulder pads, the shirtband bow!   *Russeks adv. in the Times.*

I CAME down the sixth-floor corridor of the Arbogast Building, past the World Wide Noodle Corporation, Zwinger & Rumsey, Accountants, and the Ace Secretarial Service, Mimeographing Our Specialty. The legend on the ground-glass panel next door said, "Atlas Detective Agency,

15

Noonan & Driscoll," but Snapper Driscoll had retired two years before with a .38 slug between the shoulders, donated by a snowbird in Tacoma, and I owned what good will the firm had. I let myself into the crummy anteroom we kept to impress clients, growled good morning at Birdie Claflin.

"Well, you certainly look like something the cat dragged in," she said. She had a quick tongue. She also had eyes like dusty lapis lazuli, taffy hair, and a figure that did things to me. I kicked open the bottom drawer of her desk, let two inches of rye trickle down my craw, kissed Birdie square on her lush, red mouth, and set fire to a cigarette.

"I could go for you, sugar," I said slowly. Her face was veiled, watchful. I stared at her ears, liking the way they were joined to her head. There was something complete about them; you knew they were there for keeps. When you're a private eye, you want things to stay put.

"Any customers?"

"A woman by the name of Sigrid Bjornsterne said she'd be back. A looker."

"Swede?"

16

"She'd like you to think so."

I nodded toward the inner office to indicate that I was going in there, and went in there. I lay down on the davenport, took off my shoes, and bought myself a shot from the bottle I kept underneath. Four minutes later, an ash blonde with eyes the color of unset opals, in a Nettie Rosenstein basic black dress and a baum-marten stole, burst in. Her bosom was heaving and it looked even better that way. With a gasp she circled the desk, hunting for some place to hide, and then, spotting the wardrobe where I keep a change of bourbon, ran into it. I got up and wandered out into the anteroom. Birdie was deep in a crossword puzzle.

"See anyone come in here?"

"Nope." There was a thoughtful line between her brows. "Say, what's a five-letter word meaning 'trouble'?"

"Swede," I told her, and went back inside. I waited the length of time it would take a small, not very bright boy to recite *Ozymandias*, and, inching carefully along the wall, took a quick gander out the window. A thin galoot with stooping shoulders was being very busy reading a paper outside the Gristede store two blocks away. He hadn't been there an hour ago, but then, of course, neither had I. He wore a size seven dove-colored hat from Browning King, a tan Wilson Brothers shirt with pale-blue stripes, a J. Press foulard with a mixed-red-and-white figure, dark blue Interwoven socks, and an unshined pair of ox-blood London Character shoes. I let a cigarette burn down between my fingers until it made a small red mark, and then I opened the wardrobe.

"Hi," the blonde said lazily. "You Mike Noonan?" I made a noise that could have been "Yes," and waited. She yawned. I thought things over, decided to play it safe. I yawned. She yawned back, then, settling into a corner of the wardrobe, went to sleep. I let another cigarette burn down until it made a second red mark beside the first one, and then I woke her up. She sank into a chair, crossing a pair of gams that tightened my throat as I peered under the desk at them.

"Mr. Noonan," she said, "you—you've got to help me."

"My few friends call me Mike," I said pleasantly.

18

"Mike." She rolled the syllable on her tongue. "I don't believe I've ever heard that name before. Irish?"

"Enough to know the difference between a gossoon and a bassoon."

"What *is* the difference?" she asked. I dummied up; I figured I wasn't giving anything away for free. Her eyes narrowed. I shifted my two hundred pounds slightly, lazily set fire to a finger, and watched it burn down. I could see sh : was admiring the interplay of muscles in n y shoulders. There wasn't any extra fat on Mike Noonan, but I wasn't telling *her* that. I was playing it safe until I knew where we stood.

When she spoke again, it came with a rush. "Mr. Noonan, he thinks I'm trying to poison him. But I swear the herring was pink—I took it out of the jar myself. If I could only find out how they tinted it. I offered them money, but they wouldn't tell."

"Suppose you take it from the beginning," I suggested.

She drew a deep breath. "You've heard of the golden spintria of Hadrian?" I shook my head.

19

"It's a tremendously valuable coin believed to have been given by the Emperor Hadrian to one of his proconsuls, Caius Vitellius. It disappeared about 150 A.D., and eventually passed into the possession of Hucbald the Fat. After the sack of Adrianople by the Turks, it was loaned by a man named Shapiro to the court physician, or hakim, of Abdul Mahmoud. Then it dropped out of sight for nearly five hundred years, until last August, when a deal in second-hand books named Lloyd Thursday so d it to my husband."

"And now it's gone again," I finished.

"No," she said. "At least, it was lying on the dresser when I left, an hour ago." I leaned back, pretending to fumble a carbon out of the desk, and studied her legs again. This was going to be a lot more intricate than I had thought. Her voice got huskier. "Last night I brought home a jar of Smorgasbits for Walter's dinner. You know them?"

"Small mouth-size pieces of herring and of pinkish tones, aren't they?"

Her eyes darkened, lightened, got darker again. "How did you know?"

20

"I haven't been a private op nine years for nothing, sister. Go on."

"I—I knew right away something was wrong when Walter screamed and upset his plate. I tried to tell him the herring was supposed to be pink, but he carried on like a madman. He's been suspicious of me since—well, ever since I made him take out that life insurance."

"What was the face amount of the policy?"

"A hundred thousand. But it carried a triple-indemnity clause in case he died by sea food. Mr. Noonan—Mike"—her tone caressed me—"I've got to win back his confidence. You could find out how they tinted that herring."

"What's in it for me?"

"Anything you want." The words were a whisper. I leaned over, poked open her handbag, counted off five grand.

"This'll hold me for a while," I said. "If I need any more, I'll beat my spoon on the high chair." She got up. "Oh, while I think of it, how does this golden spintria of yours tie in with the herring?"

"It doesn't," she said calmly. "I just threw it in

for glamour." She trailed past me in a cloud of scent that retailed at ninety rugs the ounce. I caught her wrist, pulled her up to me.

"I go for girls named Sigrid with opal eyes," I said.

"Where'd you learn my name?"

"I haven't been a private snoop twelve years for nothing, sister."

"It was nine last time."

"It seemed like twelve till *you* came along." I held the clinch until a faint wisp of smoke curled out of her ears, pushed her through the door. Then I slipped a pint of rye into my stomach and a heater into my kick and went looking for a bookdealer named Lloyd Thursday. I knew he had no connection with the herring caper, but in my business you don't overlook anything.

The thin galoot outside Gristede's had taken a powder when I got there; that meant we were no longer playing girls' rules. I hired a hack to Wanamaker's, cut over to Third, walked up toward Fourteenth. At Twelfth a mink-faced jasper made up as a street cleaner tailed me for a block, drifted into a dairy restaurant. At Thirteenth somebody

22

dropped a sour tomato out of a third-story window, missing me by inches. I doubled back to Wanamaker's, hopped a bus up Fifth to Madison Square, and switched to a cab down Fourth, where the second-hand bookshops elbow each other like dirty urchins.

A flabby hombre in a Joe Carbondale rope-knit sweater, whose jowl could have used a shave, quit giggling over the Heptameron long enough to tell me he was Lloyd Thursday. His shoe-button eyes became opaque when I asked to see any first editions or incunabula relative to the *Clupea harengus*, or common herring.

"You got the wrong pitch, copper," he snarled. "That stuff is hotter than Pee Wee Russell's clarinet."

"Maybe a sawbuck'll smarten you up," I said. I folded one to the size of a postage stamp, scratched my chin with it. "There's five yards around for anyone who knows why those Smorgasbits of Sigrid Bjornsterne's happened to be pink." His eyes got crafty.

"I might talk for a grand."

"Start dealing." He motioned toward the back.

I took a step forward. A second later a Roman candle exploded inside my head and I went away from there. When I came to, I was on the floor with a lump on my sconce the size of a lapwing's egg and big Terry Tremaine of Homicide was bending over me.

"Someone sapped me," I said thickly. "His name was—"

"Webster," grunted Terry. He held up a dog-eared copy of Merriam's Unabridged. "You tripped on a loose board and this fell off a shelf on your think tank."

"Yeah?" I said skeptically. "Then where's Thursday?" He pointed to the fat man lying across a pile of erotica. "He passed out cold when he saw you cave." I covered up, let Terry figure it any way he wanted. I wasn't telling him what cards I held. I was playing it safe until I knew all the angles.

In a seedy pharmacy off Astor Place, a stale Armenian whose name might have been Vulgarian but wasn't dressed my head and started asking questions. I put my knee in his groin and he lost interest. Jerking my head toward the coffee

24

urn, I spent a nickel and the next forty minutes doing some heavy thinking. Then I holed up in a phone booth and dialled a clerk I knew called Little Farvel in a delicatessen store on Amsterdam Avenue. It took a while to get the dope I wanted because the connection was bad and Little Farvel had been dead two years, but we Noonans don't let go easily.

By the time I worked back to the Arbogast Building, via the Weehawken ferry and the George Washington Bridge to cover my tracks, all the pieces were in place. Or so I thought up to the point she came out of the wardrobe holding me between the sights of her ice-blue automatic.

"Reach for the stratosphere, gumshoe." Sigrid Bjornsterne's voice was colder than Horace Greeley and Little Farvel put together, but her clothes were plenty calorific. She wore a forest-green suit of Hockanum woollens, a Knox Wayfarer, and baby crocodile pumps. It was her blouse, though, that made tiny red hairs stand up on my knuckles. Its deep yoke folds, shoulder pads, and shirtband bow could only have been designed by some master craftsman, some Cézanne of the shears.

25

"Well, Nosy Parker," she sneered, "so you found out how they tinted the herring."

"Sure—grenadine," I said easily. "You knew it all along. And you planned to add a few grains of oxylbutane-cheriphosphate, which turns the same shade of pink in solution, to your husband's portion, knowing it wouldn't show in the postmortem. Then you'd collect the three hundred g's and join Harry Pestalozzi in Nogales till the heat died down. But you didn't count on me."

"You?" Mockery nicked her full-throated laugh. "What are you going to do about it?"

"This." I snaked the rug out from under her and she went down in a swirl of silken ankles. The bullet whined by me into the ceiling as I vaulted over the desk, pinioned her against the wardrobe.

"Mike." Suddenly all the hatred had drained away and her body yielded to mine. "Don't turn me in. You cared for me—once."

"It's no good, Sigrid. You'd only double-time me again."

"Try me."

"O.K. The shirtmaker who designed your blouse —what's his name?" A shudder of fear went over her; she averted her head. "He's famous on two continents. Come on Sigrid, they're your dice."

"I won't tell you. I can't. It's a secret between this—this department store and me."

"They wouldn't be loyal to *you*. They'd sell you out fast enough."

"Oh, Mike, you mustn't. You don't know what you're asking."

"For the last time."

"Oh, sweetheart, don't you see?" Her eyes were tragic pools, a cenotaph to lost illusions. "I've got so little. Don't take that away from me. I—I'd never be able to hold up my head in Russeks again."

"Well, if that's the way you want to play it . . ." There was silence in the room, broken only by Sigrid's choked sob. Then, with a strangely empty feeling, I uncradled the phone and dialled Spring 7-3100.

For an hour after they took her away, I sat alone in the taupe-colored dusk, watching lights come on and a woman in the hotel opposite adjusting a garter. Then I treated my tonsils to five fingers of firewater, jammed on my hat, and made

27

for the anteroom. Birdie was still scowling over her crossword puzzle. She looked up crookedly at me.

"Need me any more tonight?"

"No." I dropped a grand or two in her lap. "Here, buy yourself some stardust."

"Thanks, I've got my quota." For the first time I caught a shadow of pain behind her eyes. "Mike, would—would you tell me something?"

"As long as it isn't clean," I flipped to conceal my bitterness.

"What's an eight-letter word meaning 'sentimental'?"

"Flatfoot, darling," I said, and went out into the rain.

NASAL-HAPPY MAMMA, DON'T YOU TRY TO TWO-TIME ME

ONE day not long ago, idling through the pages of a sophisticated 35-cent monthly while waiting for the barber to give me my sophisticated 65-cent monthly haircut, I was suddenly oppressed by the characteristic shortness of breath, mingled with giddiness and general trepidation, that results whenever one gets too near an advertisement for Tabu. This exotic scent, in case you have been fortunate enough to forget it, is widely publicized as "the 'Forbidden' Perfume," which means, when all the meringue is sluiced away, that it is forbidden to anyone who doesn't have $18.50 for an

29

ounce of it. The language used to describe Tabu is a chutney compounded of Pierre Loti and the Symbolist poets, so fiery that it sets every nerve aquiver, particularly those controlling the process of regurgitation. "Tabu," pants the copywriter, "a sultry, heady, lid-lowering fragrance that has whispered its way around the globe . . . intriguing as a suppressed book . . . exciting as a locked door . . . heady, sultry, confusing . . . smoulders for weeks on your gowns or furs, becoming more and more tantalizing all the while. In fact," he sniggers, leaning forward until his eyes become mere slits in his unattractive face, "until recently, Tabu came secretly from Abroad." This tender confidence appears to me romantic but somewhat unguarded; when I was a débutante, the United States Customs had pronounced views about smuggling contraband in your girdle.

The rhapsodic text of the advertisement, however, is mere frosting for its art work, which I assume is an attempt to crystallize the elusive quality of Tabu. Two citizens in evening dress, engaged in a refined musicale, have apparently experienced a common libidinal drive and fused

30

in a fierce embrace before a piano. The ardor of the pair is well-nigh volcanic. The gentleman's hair cascades down his forehead and he holds a violin at arm's length as though to pulverize it in his fingers; the lady, her wrists trailing the piano keys, is bent backward in an arc recalling the Camel Walk of 1922. It seems a pity that the Tabu people, while they were so busy stirring the senses, could not have provided some slight clue to a glamorous situation. What provoked it? Had a drop of the sultry, lid-lowering essence whispered its way around the young woman's corsage, ultimately driving her cavalier to distraction? Or is the caress itself taboo for some undisclosed reason? In fine, I resent being inflamed by a pack of upstart perfumers. They play the coquette in the taxicab and, once in the foyer, twist out of my grasp with a casual "Well, call me up soon, won't you, dear boy?"

In an effort to reduce my blood pressure, but always retaining a spirit of stern scientific inquiry, I submit the following a-priori explanation of the circumstances. Anyone interested in the amateur rights of this harlequinade, for production at

31

schools and churches, should have his head examined.

[*Scene: A suburban living room on the Main Line. As the curtain rises, Mavis Huntoon, thirty-three and disillusioned, sits at her Bechstein playing a Chopin étude. Robin Huntoon, a stolid, unimaginative man of forty who lives only for hardware, is seated in a Sleepy Hollow chair fondling some screws and hinges. After a moment, Mavis rises restlessly and moves to the French windows at rear.*]

MAVIS (*wistfully*): It's raining again.

ROBIN: Forty-five thousand, three hundred and eleven . . . forty-five thousand, three hundred and twelve . . .

MAVIS: What are you doing?

ROBIN: I'm counting my money. (*With an involuntary shudder of disgust, Mavis picks up a limp-leather volume.*)

MAVIS (*reading*):

O swallow, sister, O fleeting swallow,
My heart in me is a molten ember
And over my head the waves have met.

ROBIN: Hot spit. What's that?

32

MAVIS (*wearily*): You wouldn't understand. It's Swinburne.

ROBIN: Swinburne? I knew a Nate Swinburne once. He ran a hardware store in Mystic, Connecticut. . . . Why, what's the matter?

MAVIS (*with a strangled sob*): I can't stand it! I'm stifling here!

ROBIN: It *is* kind of close, now you mention it. I'll open a window.

MAVIS (*coming up close to him*): Robin, don't you notice anything different about me?

ROBIN (*sniffing*): Hm-m-m. Why, yes, you've got a funny smell.

MAVIS: Don't you find me heady, sultry, confusing?

ROBIN: No. (*Critically*) But you've put on a lot of weight lately.

MAVIS: Have I?

ROBIN: You certainly have. You're as big as a house. And your slip is showing.

MAVIS: I'm not wearing a slip.

ROBIN: Well, it would show if you were.

MAVIS: Anything else?

ROBIN: Maybe I shouldn't call attention to it.

33

Mavis: No, no, darling. By all means call attention to it.

Robin: You're getting wrinkles under the eyes. And a scraggly neck, like a turkey.

Mavis: Not much gets past you, does it?

Robin (*comfortably*): I guess I'm just about as wide awake as anybody in the hardware business.

Mavis: Well, look again. You've missed something.

Robin (*starting*): Why, you're holding a little gun.

Mavis: Aha. And now I pull back this gadget on top.

Robin: What are you doing that for?

Mavis: We call it "fanning back the hammer." (*She drills Robin neatly between the eyes. As she breaks the breech and thoughtfully extracts the shell, the doorbell sounds. With a moue of distaste, Mavis takes Robin by the necktie and rolls him behind the davenport. Then, applying a hint of Tabu to her lobes, she crosses to the door. Locksley Mendoza enters, wrapped in an Inverness cape. His handsome face is lean, coolly ironic, bronzed by tropical suns. As Mavis moves wordlessly to her*

34

Bechstein, Mendoza whips out a priceless Amati from its case and they launch into Jocelyn's "Berceuse." Suddenly a harsh oath escapes his lips; he drops the bow, seizes Mavis in a grip of wool.)

MENDOZA: *Sapristi!* You turn a man's bones to water inside his skin, you she-devil.

MAVIS (*struggling*): Oh, my very dear, you can't—you mustn't. It is "taboo."

MENDOZA: "Taboo"? When two people are loving each other until the seams are coming apart in the clothes, it is "taboo"?

MAVIS: No, no, it cannot be.

MENDOZA (*hoarsely*): I tell you the blood is boiling in my veins! You are a candy store filled with luscious nougats, a henhouse from which the pullets have yet to be stolen!

MAVIS: Promise me one thing. Whatever happens—whatever they should tell you about me—we'll always have this moment together.

MENDOZA: *Parbleu!* Do you think I am a milksap, that you can put me off with your bobbery? What stands between us—this man's foot sticking out from behind the davenport?

MAVIS: Of course not. It's—well—it's that

you're not the man I thought you were. Who are you, anyway?

MENDOZA (*simply*): The exterminator.

MAVIS: Then why the violin?

MENDOZA: Just an attention-getter. Nowadays you got to dramatize yourself. (*Extracting a pasteboard box*) Can I interest you in our new brand of bedbug powder? It's a ripsnorter.

MAVIS: (*sadly*): I think not. After all, *mon vieux*, in a sense we're competitors.

MENDOZA: But how?

MAVIS (*gently*): You see, darling I'm something of an exterminator myself. (*As she produces her heater and fans back the hammer a second time*)

CURTAIN

WHITE BIMBO, OR, THROUGH DULLEST AFRICA WITH THREE SLEEPY PEOPLE

TAKE one thing with another, there are few places I know better than the heart of Africa. Set me down in Bechuanaland or the Cameroons and I will find my way home with less difficulty than I would from Rittenhouse Square or Boylston Street. My entire youth, in a sense, was spent on the dark Continent. By the time I was eleven, I was probably the world's foremost authority on the works of Sir H. Rider Haggard, or at least the foremost eleven-year-old authority in Providence, Rhode Island. My impersonation of Allan Quater-

main tracking down a spoor was so exact and so
forthright that a popular movement sprang up
among my fellow-citizens to send me to Mombasa. I was, however, not quite ready for Mombasa
and begged off. At fifteen, I could quote Living-
stone and Paul Du Chaillu so glibly that my
sponsors revived their project, this time offering
to send me to Tanganyika. It became sort of a
good-humored tug of war to get me out of New
England. I don't want to sound chesty, but I suppose I've done more harm to Africa in my day
than Cecil Rhodes.

It came as a pang, therefore, to learn that my
achievement had been overshadowed by that of a
complete unknown, a person whose name occurs
in no encyclopedia or reference work on Africa.
Armand Brigaud may well be a familiar figure in
the Explorers Club, and he can probably be found
any afternoon at the National Geographic Society
swapping yarns with William Beebe and Burton
Holmes. Frankly, I never heard of him until yesterday, when I picked up a yellowing copy of a
pulp magazine called *Jungle Stories* and read his
novelette, *Killers on Safari*. Though it costs me an

effort, I shall give the man his due. In *Killers on Safari*, Armand Brigaud has written finis to the subject of Africa. After him, the deluge. Me, I'll have a double deluge with very little soda, please.

To be quite candid, the safari the author celebrates in his title is about as exciting as a streetcar journey from New Haven to Savin Rock, and his flora and fauna suggest the lobby display accompanying a Monogram jungle film. What lifts *Killers on Safari* from the ruck is a cast of characters out of Daisy Ashford by Fenimore Cooper, with Superman acting as accoucheur. Their adventures are recorded in some of the most stylish prose to flow out of an inkwell since Helen Hunt Jackson's *Ramona*. The people of Mr. Brigaud's piece, beset by hostile aborigines, snakes, and blackwater fever, converse with almost unbearable elegance, rolling out their periods like Edmund Burke. Here, for example, Diana Patten and Walter Huntley, a couple of the characters, in a sylvan glade, as their porters take a short breather:

"A coarse forest pig shuffled out of a ravine and began nibbling on a bamboo root. The shapely hand of Diana Patten made a gesture which encompassed the whole scene as she said softly: 'These beasts of the wilderness know when it is safe for them to come near the most murderous of all mammals: man!' Walter Huntley stared adoringly at her symmetrical features, which became so girlish and gentle when her red lips parted in a smile. For the thousandth time he thought that she was unusually tall, but breathtakingly gorgeous, from her wavy blonde hair down her statuesque body to her shapely feet. The big pig trotted back into the ravine."

This tropical idyll pauses for approximately twelve hundred words of exposition to establish Diana's and Walter's identity, and then:

"The forest hog emerged again from the ravine, leading a sow and four piglets. 'Are they not coarse, rough, and as perfectly alike as rain drops in every detail excepting size?' Diana chuckled, snuggling against Walter's shoulder." I cannot recall a more engaging passage in fiction, and I've been trying for almost eighteen seconds.

The principals of *Killers on Safari* are three: Dr. Hargrave, a goatish New York physician traveling through Sierra Leone on a scientific mission vaguely elated to rejuvenation; Walter Huntley, his guide, a former patron of alcoholic beverages, seeking salvation; and Diana Patten, the doctor's nurse. Judged by ordinary hospital standards, Diana is the least conventional nurse ever sent out by a registry. The decorative heading represents her as a toothsome showgirl, clad in a minute swatch of rayon and transfixing a gigantic black warrior with an assagai. "As a student in a women's college, she had won prizes in archery and javelin-throwing contests," Mr. Brigaud fluently explains. Diana, in all justice, has her softer side; somewhat later, when she and Walter are rushed by a savage, she cries out instinctively, "Don't kill him, but put a bullet into one of his legs!" Diana's innate sentimentality continually gets in her way; further on, a black chieftain named Wambogo invites her to share his pallet and she taunts him into duelling with javelins, with this result: "It would have been easy for her to disembowel Wambobo before the latter could bring his own spear into play. But she preferred to maim him. . . . Therefore she split open Wambogo's breast muscles, and cut his tendons under his armpit. Then,

41

as he howled with pain and rage, she slid out of his grasp, leaped back, and pinked him through a leg." Lucky for Wambogo that Diana was only pettish, or she might really have unsheathed her claws.

The story opens with Diana warning Walter that their employer, Dr. Hargrave, has become jealous of their attachment and means him no good. Her apprehensions are justified, for the Doctor is everlastingly crouched in the shrubbery, tremulous with desire, cooking up schemes for eliminating the guide. At length he eggs on a treacherous native named Itira Nlembi to ambush Walter, but the latter draws first claret and the aggressor slinks off into the potted palms with the equivalent of a broken neck. The party now proceeds sluggishly to the territory of a tribe of fierce hallboys called the Amutu, where Dr. Hargrave divides his time between healing the sick and pinching Diana. She finds his attentions odious and haughtily terms him a boor. Dr. Hargrave smarts under the insult:

" 'So I am called a boor!' he mouthed angrily. 'I begin to have enough of your sponsoring the cause of the former tramp, Miss Patten!' And turning on his heels, he strode furiously toward the central pavilion. . . . When the portly bulk of Hargrave disappeared behind the lap [*sic*] of the pavilion acting as a door, her spirits sank and she moaned: 'From bad to worse! It is bad, very bad, to be under orders of a man on the verge of insanity! I wonder how it will all end!' " It all ends quite spiritedly, with Hargrave putting a slug in the guide's ribs and Walter bringing his revolver butt down on the Doctor's skull. This surprisingly restores good-fellowship all around, and the rivals unite to repulse an attack by the Amutu. Hargrave herewith exits untidily from the plot, struck down by a battle axe, but thanks to a homemade avalanche and some fast spear work by Diana, Walter and the girl get clear. It then transpires how foresighted Diana was to major in archery at college; she keeps the larder well stocked with antelope meat and liquidates a black leopard who waylays her in the greenery. Some index of her pluck on this occasion may be gained from Walter's words following the event:

" 'You acted with amazing spunk and skill.

You are a marvelous heroine. But, damn it! For a moment I nearly got a stroke at the thought that that awful lion was about to tear you to shreds!' " He implores Diana not to go hunting unescorted in future, but, womanlike, she disregards him and sallies forth. Thereupon her lover behaves much in the manner of a Keystone two-reeler: "Walter tore his hat from his head, slammed it on the ground, and kicked it." Whether he jumped up and down on it or flung a custard pie after her is not indicated. His blood pressure again starts vaulting when a courier reports that Diana has been taken captive by Itira Nlembi: "Walter saw blood on his face, and on one of his arms, and almost got a stroke." Walter, in fact, constantly appears to be hovering on the edge of a syncope; the next time he sees Diana, in Itira's lair, he reacts characteristically: "Walter nearly became apoplectic at the sight of her dishevelled hair, bruised arms, and torn clothes." My knowledge of hypertension is elementary, but it seems to me Walter would be far better off rocking on the porch of a New Jersey milk farm than mousing around Sierra Leone.

44

The story (for want of a better term) now develops what is unquestionably the tiniest crescendo in the annals of modern typesetting. Itira Nlembi, overcome by Diana's charms, offers to make her his queen. Diana responds in her usual polished forensic style: " 'I have been waiting for some hare-brained proposals ever since your evil-smelling grub-eaters ambushed and overcame me by sheer strength of numbers!' " Nevertheless, playing for time, she pretends to accede on condition that he court her for two months, as befits a lady of rank. Itira, anxious not to breach the rules of etiquette, assents. Then, aided by two ladies of the harem, the lovers vamoose and race to meet a British relief column they have magically notified. Itira's hatchetmen, of course, give pursuit. At the couple's darkest hour, just as Walter's arteries are snapping like pipestems, comes deliverance: "Walter's calm voice was belied by the feverish look of his eyes and his twitching lips. Suddenly he beamed ecstatically and shouted at the top of his lungs: 'Oh, my dear, there will be no reason of hurting that pretty head of yours! Look down there, toward the north! Don't you see gun barrels

45

gleaming under the sun? They are coming, the British!' " A few rounds of grape disperse the blacks, and the British officer in command benignly advises Walter and Diana to get themselves to the nearest chaplain. " 'And,' he adds, with a gruff chuckle, "could I be best man? I sort of think it would round up my memories of this chapter of adventures spiced by human interest.' "

And so, as apoplexy and archery join lips under the giant clichés and Kipling spins in his grave like a lathe, let us bid adieu to Armand Brigaud, a great kid and a great story teller. See you around Lake Chad, old boy, and don't take any wooden rhetoric.

SO LITTLE TIME
MARCHES ON

Marquand's principal contact with Hollywood was in 1941, when *H. M. Pulham, Esquire* was produced by King Vidor for M-G-M and Marquand went to the Coast to work on the dialog. On Dec. 4, 1941 the film was released at a dual "world première" in Loew's State and Loew's Tremont Theaters in Boston. . . . Marquand was rushed around from one press conference to another and photographed wearing a sad smile as he presented to a Harvard librarian the original movie script. Marquand got back to New York from the world premiere with a slight cold and a nervous feeling that something drastic was about to happen. Two days later the Japanese attacked Pearl Harbor.—*From Roger Butterfield's biography of J. P. Marquand in* Life.

OUT of these things, and many more, is woven the warp and woof of my childhood memory: the dappled sunlight on the great lawns of Chowderhead, our summer estate at Newport, the bittersweet fragrance of stranded eels at low tide, the alcoholic breath of a clubman wafted on the breeze from Bailey's Beach. That my family was fantastically wealthy I was early aware, although good taste naturally forbade any excessive display. My father occasionally appeared at table in sack suits checkered with dollar signs, and the gardeners used rubies instead of gravel on the paths, but the guest who so far forgot himself as to exclaim "Hot puppies!" and fill his pockets with the baubles was rarely invited again. One of my first distinct recollections is of watching the men burn leaves under the giant elms and my momentary surprise when I found that they were not leaves but old banknotes. I felt then, with the kind of intuition children alone know, that my lot would be different from that of my fellows.

Almost from the moment of birth, it seems to me, I was passionately fond of books; before I was quite five, I devoured in a single afternoon Doughty's *Arabia Deserta*, the Pandects of Justinian (in translation, of course), and the novels of Mrs. Aphra Behn, a piece of gluttony that ultimately involved the services of three stomach specialists from the Massachusetts General Hos-

48

pital. It was this youthful predilection for belles lettres that first brought me into conflict with my father. He had been reading *The Private Papers of Henry Ryecroft* and had mislaid it. Fearful lest I might have eaten it, he invaded the nursery and demanded, "Have you noticed any Gissing around here?" "No, sir," I replied submissively, "but I saw you pinching Nannie in the linen closet." He frowned thoughtfully and withdrew, leaving me prey to a strange uneasiness. Four days later, Italy declared war on Tripoli.

Though life at Chowderhead was spacious, to say the least, my father did not believe in pampering the young, and constantly strove to imbue in me a sense of frugality. Until I was eight, I received an allowance of five cents a month, for which I was held strictly accountable. Of course, five cents in those days bought a good deal more than it does now; it bought a firkin of gherkins or a ramekin of fescue or a pipkin of halvah, but since I was expected to furnish my own clothes out of this sum, I had little left for luxuries. I well recall my bitterness when I discovered that the small hoard of pennies I had accumulated over the summer

49

was missing from my knickerbockers. There had been a series of minor peculations at home that year and I suspected the housekeeper's son, a rather ferret-faced lad. I wrung a confession from him, and, to teach the pickpocket a lesson, plunged his head repeatedly into the bay. As luck would have it, my father happened along at this juncture. His jaw dropped. "What are you doing there, young man?" he snapped. "Well, guv'nor," I chuckled, "I guess you might say I was taking a little dip in the ocean." Retrieving his jaw, my father continued his constitutional with a glance that boded me no good. Nine days later, Bosnia severed relations with Herzegovina.

If my father prided himself on anything, it was his unconventional theories about education. To him the customary progression from the grammar grades through high school to college was so much poppycock. Consequently, when I was eight, I was apprenticed to the proprietor of a delicatessen store in Portland, Maine, to acquire worldly experience before entering a university. The nine exciting years I spent under the tutelage of genial Ned Harnischfeger did more to mold my character than anything I could possibly imagine. As I wrapped a succulent cut of smoked salmon for a customer, Ned would painstakingly describe the topography of Nova Scotia, the tides in the Bay of Fundy, and the dynamics of spawning; a corned-beef sandwich on rye was a handy pretext for a lecture on domestic cattle, cereal grains, or the general subject of indigestion. My Portland phase terminated in a curious fashion. One noon I was busily filling orders behind the counter. Suddenly, out of the corner of my eye, I saw Grimalkin, our mouser, leap upon a table, seize a customer's lunch, and bolt out into the alley. The customer, thunder-struck, stammered forth some inarticulate comment. "What's the matter, stupid?" I demanded roughly. "Has the cat got your tongue sandwich?" He went scarlet. I saw Harnischfeger's lips tighten and I knew subconsciously that a turning point in my life was at hand. Two days later, Georges Carpentier climbed into the ring at Boyle's Thirty Acres and I entered Harvard.

From the beginning I was recognized as a leader in my class, one of the few whose destiny it is to inspire and guide their less gifted mates. (I often

51

say that college is a microcosm, a tiny world in which is foreshadowed the turbulence of actual life. That is what I often say.) My freshman year, unluckily, was marred by family dissension. Unbeknownst to me, violent quarrels were raging at home, my mother accusing my father of pettiness and cupidity. At last she could abide his stinginess no longer and departed for Reno. The news reached me, oddly enough, during a French class, as we were translating an absorbing passage of Erckmann-Chatrian. His face grave, the instructor halted the lesson and read aloud a curt message stating that my mother had left home because of my father's avarice. "I hope this isn't too much of a shock, old man," he said sympathetically. "No, that's the way of the world," I replied. "Money makes the *mère* go." An expression I could not fathom clouded the instructor's face and I was oppressed by a vague sense of disaster. Three days later a society bridge expert named Joseph B. Elwell padded downstairs with a sleepy yawn, bringing an era to a close.

It would be both immodest and redundant to detail the triumphs I scored in the balance of my

52

stay at Cambridge. Suffice it to say that I won what paltry distinctions the gridiron, the diamond, and the debating platform could afford, not to mention completing the usual academic course in two and a half years. In one single instance did I come off second best, and then because I disdained to take unfair advantage of a rival in love. The latter was an immensely rich young Corsican upperclassman whose successes with the opposite sex were well-nigh as spectacular as my own. On the surface my relations with César Sporchini were friendly. We often sent each other a dancing girl or a dozen of Imperial Tokay, but we both knew who would be victor if our blades crossed. One evening, at the Old Howard Burlesque, we were both smitten with the same pair of captivating blue eyes. I subsequently persuaded their owner to share a cozy lobster-and-champagne supper in a private dining room at Locke Ober's. Despite the fabulous string of pearls I slyly insinuated under her plate, the silly creature remained obdurate. Again and again, in the weeks that followed, I plied her with gifts, only to discover that Sporchini was outbidding me

53

for her favor. The Homeric struggle that ensued is still a legend in the chop houses along Scollay Square. At length, sacrificing heavens knows what vineyards and olive groves, Sporchini presented the fair tyrant with a solid-gold Stutz Bearcat and she yielded up her tawdry charms. I received word that I had been worsted with a philosophical shrug. "Oh, well," I observed, brushing a nascent mustache with my pinkie in the manner of the late Lew Cody, "Money makes the Margot." My roommate stiffened and emitted a cryptic grunt that somehow filled me with anxiety. Five days later, Harry C. Klemfuss, the press agent for Campbell's Funeral Home, formally announced the passing of Rodolpho Alfonzo Raffaelo Pierre Filibert Guglielmi di Valentina d'Antonguolla, better known as "Rudy" Valentino.

The strident note of a distant banjo was stilled, the echo of undergraduate voices in the corridors hushed at last. It was time for me to face stern realities, to take over the reins of my father's vast industrial empire. Yet somehow I hungered for a creative outlet instead of the sordid money grubbing that awaited me. Acting on impulse at the

54

eleventh hour, I joined a strolling Shakespearean troupe. For a time I was a mere supernumerary and fourth assistant stage manager. Then a dazzling stroke of fortune presented a chance to play a really important rôle. On the afternoon we were to give *Othello*, the leading man demanded an increase in salary. Denied it, he resigned in a temper. Shortly afterward, I encountered our impresario seated in the darkened auditorium, head buried in his hands. "I picked him up from the gutter!" he wailed. "I don't understand it!" "It's simple enough," I comforted him. "Money makes the Moor go." He looked up sharply and there was a challenge in his eyes that set my heart racing. One day later, Frances "Peaches" Browning sued for divorce and my theatrical career was a thing of the past.

And there, on the very threshold of life, face to face with the rich, dark promise of the years that lay ahead, let us leave me. Except for the beauty of Apollo and the mind of a Jesuit, I had scant equipment for the struggle: a trifling million or two in tax-free bonds, a leaky old yacht, a great, drafty mansion on Fifth Avenue peopled by ghosts. The Turgid Thirties were dawning, bringing with them the depression, Henry Luce, and, above all, the outsize picture magazine. A sense of prophecy was not enough. From now on I must learn how to duck.

WHOSE LADY NICOTINE?

At approximately four o'clock yesterday afternoon, the present troubadour, a one-story taxpayer in a wrinkled alpaca jacket and a repossessed Panama, was gaping into the window of Alfred Buntwell Inc., the celebrated tobacconist in Radio City. Above his balding, gargoyle head floated a feathery cloud containing a Mazda bulb labeled "Idea!" Buntwell is a name revered by pipe smokers everywhere; his briars have probably penetrated farther into the earth's far places than the Union Jack. From the steaming jungles of the Gran Chaco to the snows of Kanchanjanga, from the Hook of Holland to the Great Barrier Reef, the white dot on the Buntwell pipe stem is the

57

sign of the sahib. Deep in equatorial Africa, surrounded by head-hunters, Mungo Park clenched a Buntwell pipe between his teeth to maintain his fortitude; it was a battered Buntwell mouthpiece that yielded up the fate of the Franklin polar expedition.

Peering into the shop, jostled by crisp, well-fed executives hurrying toward million-dollar deals, it suddenly struck me that a Buntwell pipe was the key to my future. Here at last was a magic talisman that would transform me from a wormy, chopfallen cipher into a forceful, grim-lipped tycoon. A wave of exultation swept over me; I saw myself in the club car of the Twentieth Century Limited puffing a silver-mounted Buntwell and merging directorates with a careless nod. I too could become one of those enviable types who lunged against knotty-pine interiors in four-color advertisements, smoking their Buntwells and fiercely demanding Old Peg-leg Whisky. "Give me Old Peg-leg's satin smoothness every time," I would growl. "I like a *blended* rye."

I squared my tiny shoulders and, baring my teeth in the half-snarl befitting a major industrial-

58

ist, entered the shrine. To my chagrin, no obse-
quious lackey sprang forward to measure my
features for the correct model. A cathedral hush
enveloped the shop, which had the restrained
elegance of a Park Avenue jeweler's. At a chaste
showcase displaying a box of panatelas marked
down to a thousand dollars, a glacial salesman
was attending a fierce old party with white cav-
alry mustaches redolent of Napoleon brandy. In
the background, another was languidly demon-
strating a cigarette lighter to a dowager weighed
down under several pounds of diamonds. I
coughed apologetically and gave the salesman a
winning smile to indicate that I knew my place.
The old grenadier scowled at me from under
beetling brows. "Confound it, sir," he roared,
"you're not at a cock fight! Blasted place is gettin'
noisier than the durbar!" I cleared my throat, in
which a fish bone had mysteriously lodged, and
made myself as inconspicuous as possible. The
salesman hastily explained that the war had
brought an influx of foreigners, but his client
refused to be mollified.

59

"Should have caned the bounder," he sputtered. "Country's goin' to the demnition bow-wows, dash it all! Now then, Harkrider, what's this infernal nonsense about my Burma cheroots?" He waved aside the salesman's excuse that a convoy had been sunk, commanded that Buntwell himself be summoned.

"But Mr. Buntwell's been dead sixty years, major," Harkrider protested.

"None of your poppycock!" barked the major. "You tell Buntwell to bring 'em around personally by noon tomorrow or I close my account!" He stamped out, his wattles crimson with rage, and I sidled forward timidly. In a few badly chosen words, I indicated that I required a pipe.

"H'm-m-m," murmured Harkrider grudgingly, surveying my clothes. "Just a moment." He disappeared through a curtain and engaged in a whispered consultation with the manager. I dimly overheard a phrase that sounded like "butter-snipe"; the two were obviously discussing their lunch. At length the salesman re-entered and conducted me sullenly to a showcase. After some deliberation, he extracted what appeared to be an

60

old sycamore root fitted with a steel flange that covered the bowl.

"Know anything about pipes?" he inquired patronizingly.

"Well, not exactly," I hesitated. "I had a corn-cob when I was a little boy——"

"I'm not interested in reminiscences of your youth," he snapped. "Hold still." With a quick gesture, he jammed the root into my mouth and backed off, studying my face critically.

"Wh-what is it for?" I stammered.

"Big-game hunting," he returned loftily. I was screwing up my courage to inquire out of which end the bullet came when he suddenly plucked it from my teeth. "No, I don't care for you in that. Let's see now—what's your club?"

"Why—er—uh—the Williams After-Shave Club," I replied politely. "You know, for men whose skins welcome that zestful, bracing tang——"

"No, no," he broke in irritably. "Where do you keep your yacht?" His face darkened and he took a threatening step forward. "You have a yacht, haven't you?"

61

"Oh—why—er—bub—certainly," I lied skill-fully. "He's—I mean, she's laid up right now, the man's scraping her chimney. It got full of sea-weeds."

Harkrider glared at me suspiciously, clearly unconvinced.

"Yo heave ho, blow the man down," I hummed nonchalantly, executing a few steps of the sailor's hornpipe. "Thar she blows and sparm at that! A double ration of plum duff for all hands, matey!" The stratagem was successful; with a baffled grunt, Harkrider produced a green velvet jewel case and exhibited a small, charred stub encrusted with salt.

"That's been used before, hasn't it?" I faltered.

"Of course it's been used," he grated. "You don't think you're going to get a new pipe for sixty-seven dollars, do you?"

"Oh, no, naturally," I agreed. "Tell you the truth, I had in mind something a bit smaller."

"Smaller?" snorted Harkrider. "You ought to have a calabash to go with that jaw of yours!"

"That's what I was telling the wife only this morning," I chuckled. "Gee, did you ever see anything like it? It's worse than an English bull-dog's."

"Well, do you want a calabash or not?" he interrupted. "They're twenty dollars—though I guess you don't see that much money in a year, do you?" Blushing like a lovely long-stemmed American Beauty rose, I explained that I merely wanted something to knock around in, a homely old jimmy pipe I could suck on while dispensing salty aphorisms like Velvet Joe. After a heart-rending plea, he finally consented to part with a factory second for thirteen dollars, equipped with an ingenious aluminum coil which conveyed the nicotine juice directly into the throat before it lost its potency. To prove my gratitude, I immediately bought a tobacco jar in the shape of a human skull, two pounds of Buntwell's Special Blend of chopped amethysts and attar of roses, and a cunning all-purpose reamer equally useful for removing carbon from a pipe or barnacles from a boat. Peeling eighty-three rugs from my skinny little roll, I caught up my purchases and coursed homeward whistling gems from The Bartered Bride. Right after dinner, I disposed myself in my favorite easy chair, lit a cheery blaze in the pipe and picked up the evening paper.

When I regained consciousness, there was a smell in the apartment like a Hindu suttee, and an angel in starched denim was taking my pulse and what remained of my roll. If I go on improving at this rate, she's promised I can get up tomorrow. That means I can go out Wednesday and go to jail on Thursday, because in the meantime I've got a date to heave a brick through a plate-glass window in Radio City. See you in Alcatraz, bud.

GARNISH YOUR FACE WITH PARSLEY AND SERVE

ON A balmy summer evening in Los Angeles two years ago, heavy with the scent of mimosa and crispy-fried noodles from the Chinese quarter, I happened to be a member of the small, select audience of cocaine peddlers, package thieves, and assorted strays at the Cozy Theatre that witnessed the world première of a remarkable motion picture called *The Sex Maniac*. Most of the production, I grieve to say, is little more than a blur in my memory, but one scene still stands out with cameolike clarity. Into the consulting room of a fairly mad physician, whose name I somehow remember as Lucas Membrane, hurtled a haggard middle-aged woman, towing her husband, a psy-

65

chotic larrikin about seven feet tall. The doctor examined the patient cursorily through a pocket lens, inspected his tongue, and, muttering "Just as I feared—dementia praecox," inoculated him intravenously with an icing gun like those commonly found in French bakeries. The patient slowly expanded, gnashing his teeth, until his head grazed the ceiling. Then he darted into the next room, where a luscious showgirl in a diaphanous shift unaccountably lay asleep on a slab, and, booming like a bittern, hustled her off into the canebrake. His wife and Dr. Membrane stared after him, shaking their heads in mild perplexity. "Well, Doc," observed the former, inflecting her words in the classic manner of Miss Beatrice Lillie, "I've seen some pretty . . . strange . . . experiments in my time, but *this* . . . is tops."

I was tempted to echo these sentiments yesterday when, in the Sunday edition of the Newark *Star-Ledger* which I received as lagniappe with fifteen cents' worth of sour tomatoes on Division Street, I ran across an arresting article on various home beauty treatments evolved by Hollywood personalities. It appears that, far from favoring

66

expensive skin foods and massage creams, our reigning film favorites prefer cosmetics drawn from their own kitchen shelves. Like Dolores Moran, for instance. Any discussion of lovely Hollywood elbows would be incomplete without a reference to hers; I myself recall more than one such discussion that seemed frustrated and sterile because no reference was made to Miss Moran's elbows. To keep them trig and alluring, the blond starlet rests them on two halves of a lemon for twenty minutes while she rehearses her lines, then rubs them satin-smooth with olive oil. Julie Bishop preserves her hands by rolling them in oatmeal (which, of course, she discards before playing her more romantic love scenes), and Ida Lupino safeguards an already creamy complexion with a poultice of powdered milk. Urging her readers to branch out for themselves, the beauty editor of the *Star-Ledger* appends several other recipes of a similar homely nature, notably a hand pack of corn meal and benzoin, an egg whipped up in lemon juice to rejuvenate tired or muddy faces, and a flocculent suspension of cornstarch in boiling water as an emollient for leathery skins.

What with a soaring luxury tax and a shrinking supply of cosmetics, it was inevitable that Elizabeth Arden would be supplanted by the grocery counter, but I am none too sure of the effect on the masculine gender. I foresee almost certain repercussions in the divorce courts and the Sunday-evening radio tribunals, and I offer the following *mise en scène* as a horoscope of what to expect shortly over any major network:

[*Scene: A radio station. John J. Antennae, spiritual father to millions, broods remotely before his microphone, pondering the philosophy of Ralph Waldo Trine and waiting for the announcer to complete his commercial. Fox-nosed, sallow, closely related to God on his mother's side, Antennae has been by turns an insurance technician, reception clerk in a cut-rate mortuary, and used-car salesman. From the side he dimly resembles a spider, an effect he tries to counteract with a ghastly veneer of benevolence.*]

ANNOUNCER: . . . So why not back up our boys in the steaming jungles of New Guinea by chewing Respighi's Bubble Gum, that amazing new blend of chicle, old tea leaves and pine shavings?

68

Remember, folks, maladroit tests by wool-gathering scientists have shown that Respighi's contains no single ingredient that could kill a horse, and even if it did, the hydrochloric acid in your system will dissolve anything. And now, Mr. Antennae, the case of Mr. M. W.

ANTENNAE (*nasally*): Step up, please. (*Milton Wefers, a dispirited taxpayer in his mid-thirties, falters to the podium.*) Very well, sir, tell us your story. (*Wefers blubbers wordlessly.*) Come, come, tears aren't going to help. Here, take my hand. Now then.

WEFERS (*brokenly*): Mr. Antennae, I first met my present wife in high school.

ANTENNAE: Just a moment. Am I to understand that you first met your present wife in high school?

WEFERS: That is correct.

ANTENNAE (*sharply*): You mean you had not met this woman—this little lady to whom you have pledged the most sacred vow the human voice can utter—previous to the time you speak of? Answer yes or no.

WEFERS: No. Well, shortly after we were married—seventeen years, five months, and four days, to be exact—I started in noticing that this party, that is, my wife, was covered with cracker meal.

ANTENNAE: Cracker meal? You don't mean Crainquebille, do you?

WEFERS (*lymphatically*): Crainquebille? What's that?

ANTENNAE: It's a story by Anatole France.

WEFERS: How could my wife be covered with a story by Anatole France?

ANTENNAE (*waspishly*): I'm the one who's asking the questions around here, Percy.

ANNOUNCER: Yes, Mr. Antennae—and friends in our listening audience—do *you* ever ask yourself the question: What am I doing to keep myself sweet and wholesome for those boys in the steaming jungles of New Guinea? It's your patriotic duty as an American to protect the home front with Respighi's, that yummy, gummy confection that irradiates the vocal cords and promotes pharyngeal fun!

ANTENNAE: All right now, go ahead with your problem.

WEFERS: So like I say, Mr. Antennae, it made me nervous my wife always wearing cracker crumbs at the table. I mean it got on my nerves. It was like living in the same house with a breaded veal cutlet.

ANTENNAE (*silkily*): I see. I take it you've had considerable experience sharing your residence with breaded veal cutlets?

WEFERS: Well, no, but I—

ANTENNAE: Tell me, young man, have you ever had any—ah—psychic disturbances? Ever been confined to an institution?

WEFERS: No, sir.

ANTENNAE: Never received a blow on the head, to the best of your recollection?

WEFERS: No, sir. Well, pretty soon I begun to watch her and I saw all kinds of things that made me suspicious. Every time I come home at night, why she would have her nose in a grapefruit.

ANTENNAE: How do you mean?

WEFERS: I mean she would be lying down with this grapefruit on her countenance. She said it took out the wrinkles.

ANNOUNCER: Yes, folks, and speaking of wrinkles, here's a new one! Did you know that every stick of Respighi's Bubble Gum is subjected

71

to six hundred pounds of live steam to bake in the invigorating freshness of the great north woods? The next time you're in a lumber yard, make this test for yourself: whittle off the end of a fresh spruce plank and chew it to a pulp. That same zestful tang of turpentine and resin comes to you in each factory-fresh packet of Respighi's, the Friendlier Gum, chosen all-time favorite by our boys in the steaming jungles of New Guinea!

ANTENNAE: Now, my friend, continue your story. You claim that this behavior on the part of your loved one caused you a feeling of anguish?

WEFERS: It did, Mr. Antennae. (*Sobbing*) I was a loving husband at all times; I was always bringing her little bags of fruit and candy and kissing her on the nape of the neck—

ANTENNAE (*hastily*): Yes, yes, no details, please. Go on with your narrative.

WEFERS: One Sunday morning I went in the kitchen and found her making some fried eggs. I thought they were for my breakfast, but instead of putting them on my plate, she placed them on her chin, like a kind of a hot compress.

ANTENNAE: You discussed the incident with her?

72

WEFERS: She stated that it would give her a firm, well-molded, youthful throat. Then I started to take some farina out of the double boiler, but she said she was saving it for her forehead. She also told me she planned to use my marmalade under her eyes to banish crow's feet.

ANTENNAE: What was the upshot of these actions?

WEFERS: Well, I couldn't stand it any longer, so I went down to the public library.

ANTENNAE: To think things out, is that it?

WEFERS: No, sir. To reread a story by Melville Davisson Post called *Corpus Delicti*.

ANTENNAE: Oh? What was this story about?

WEFERS (*bashfully*): I'd rather not say.

ANTENNAE: What transpired after that between you and your wife?

WEFERS: I'd rather not say.

ANTENNAE: You seem to have gotten pretty close-mouthed all of a sudden.

WEFERS: Yup.

ANTENNAE: Since the Sunday you speak of, has there been any substantial change in your wife?

WEFERS: Oh, boy.

73

ANTENNAE: Have you noticed anything out of the ordinary in the household?

WEFERS: Well, there was a funny smell of nitric acid in the bathroom, but it went away after a while.

ANTENNAE: And what, precisely, brings you here tonight? What is your problem?

WEFERS: Well, Mr. Antennae, I tell you. A couple of weeks ago I got interested in a certain party, a hostess in a rumba school. She returns my affection and we were wondering if we should get married.

ANTENNAE: You're sure your wife doesn't stand in the way?

WEFERS: Positive.

ANTENNAE: Well, my boy, I'm going to give you youngsters the sort of advice I don't believe I've ever given anyone before. *Go* to this person, look deep into your hearts, I beg of you, and when you've found the answer—*if* you have the courage in yourselves to face the questions that *need* answering, mind you—*make* up your minds, won't you? . . . You will? . . . (*Emotionally*) God bless you!

74

ANNOUNCER: Folks, have you ever stopped to realize how barren the world would be without a sticky glutinous blob adhering to your dentition? Do you know that in the steaming jungles of New Guinea, your boys consider Respighi's Bubble Gum their number one ration? They're counting on you, Respighi-chewers; don't let them down. It's *so* juicy—*so* tasty—and golly, we've got *so* much of it on hand!

CURTAIN

HIT HIM AGAIN, HE'S SOBER

HAD the late Henry James been standing on the steps of his house at 21 Washington Place early this morning, he would have seen the deponent, his neighbor, totter out of a cab and collapse with a sob in the arms of the night elevator man. No doubt Mr. James, who oddly enough *was* standing there gassing with Mark Twain and Richard Harding Davis, imagined he was seeing just another drunk. That is Mr. James's privilege; personally, I do not give a fig for his good opinion of me. But I do most definitely want to clarify the incident before it becomes distorted. It is typical of our sick civilization that a man as temperate as myself, abstemious to the point of fanaticism, should become the butt of gossip. And yet, paradoxically, it was my very sobriety that brought down on me vilification and physical abuse worse than was ever heaped on an early Christian martyr.

The whole wretched affair began yesterday afternoon. When the late sunlight filtered through the blinds onto my Tyrian-purple couch, it revealed a very sick man. Three Lilliputians in doublet and hose, armed with nutpicks and oyster forks, were enfilading my big toe, from which the letters "o-u-c-h" zigzagged away into infinity. During the night, parties unknown had removed my corneas, varnished and replaced them, and fitted me with a curious steel helmet, several sizes too small. Lying there cradled between softest Fruit of the Loom, a deep cocoa-flavored sense of remorse welled upward from the knees and constricted my heart.

"You mucker," I said through my teeth, "if you've an ounce of manhood in your make-up, you'll get down on all fours and beg her forgiveness." This gaudy monologue continued uninterrupted through my ablutions, except when the can of tooth powder slipped from my fingers and exploded on the floor with a roar like a fragmentation bomb. A few seconds later, I entered my wife's presence with the smug exaltation of a character out of a Hall Caine novel, clothed in a white dimity frock and a blue hair ribbon, fingering the temperance badge pinned to my breast.

"I'm through," I declaimed. "Never again. Goodby, John Barleycorn, hello, Walker-Gordon. *Mens sana in corpore sano.* Look at this hand—steady as a rock." My peach blossom looked up from her buhl writing cabinet, shrugged coldly, and resumed adding up the liquor bill. Determined to prove I had undergone a moral regeneration worthy of *Pilgrim's Progress*, I conjured up a corn popper and a volume of Colley Cibber's memoirs and snuggled down before the hearth. After I had read in silence for twenty seconds, the pica type tired my eyes and I leaned my head on my hand for support. Suddenly the phone shrilled and I arose, adroitly demolishing a vase of chrysanthemums. Two members of our young married set were holding an impromptu cocktail party. Next to Mrs. George Washington Kavanaugh, they assured me, my presence would establish it as the social event of the season. I was refusing politely but firmly when I heard my wife whinny over my shoulder.

"A party! A party!" she bleated. "You never take me to a party! I want to go to the party! Party ... party ... party ..." Before I could reason with her, she flung herself on the counterpane and started sobbing into the bolster. Aware of the futility of trying to combat tears with logic, I acceded wearily. On the way uptown in the taxi, however, I made it plain that my decision to abstain from alcohol was irrevocable. My wife's lip curled superciliously. "Tell it to Sweeney," she advised. I leaned over to Sweeney, who was beating an impatient tatoo on the steering wheel while waiting for the lights to change, and told him my decision to abstain was irrevocable. His contemptuous chuckle infuriated me, and I lost my head. "You wait, the two of you!" I screamed, hammering my tiny fists on the jump seat. "May I fall down dead if I so much as touch a drop!" I was still defying the lightning as we swept into the pleasure pavilion. Eighteen or twenty voluptuaries, in varying stages of repair, were holding

80

wassail in a cosy two-room apartment. To make the proceedings more intimate, someone had introduced a Great Dane, a parakeet, and a progressive child who was busily emptying fruit rinds and cigarette ends into the men's hats. Yet amid the sickening debauch, suggesting Babylon at its most dissolute (Babylon, Long Island, that is), I stood a figure apart, a pillar unmoved by the blandishments and mockery of my fellows.

"Just one teentsy-weentsy sip," begged my hostess, a tantalizing blonde, all black georgette and open-mesh stockings. "Don't be thataway, you inflexible boy." For a moment her dear nearness maddened me, but I resolutely averted my face and called for a glass of Adam's ale. The more turbulent the carousal, the more steadfast I became; Cromwell at his flintiest was an orchid compared to me. In my foolish pride, I believed that I had found the philosopher's stone, that I was immune from disaster. And then the Moving Finger moved. The host, a broth of a boy who had once run seventy-nine yards down the Bowl with the Harvard backfield clinging to his waist, linked arms with me.

"Going get you sandwich," he proposed indistinctly. "Come on kitchen." I rashly extricated myself and stepped away. As I did, he reached down to the vicinity of his tibia and came up with a haymaker that caught me flush on the button. An interesting display of Catherine wheels, Very lights, and star shells flashed before me, and uttering a taut "Mamma," I melted into the parquet. I awoke on a pile of krimmer coats in the bedroom to discover my wife applying a cold poultice to the sub-maxillary region. In between embrocations, the Angel of the Crimea, her cheeks aflame with Martinis, informed me that I had forever alienated us from the beau monde. I had deliberately pinched the hostess, kicked two Whitneys in the shin, and smashed a priceless collection of Royal Worcester china. I protested I was innocent, a victim of some hideous conspiracy. "I'm as sober as you are!" I pleaded. "Soberer! I haven't had a dram since yesterday!" "Yes, yes," she agreed soothingly. "Help me with him, will you, Ariadne? His legs get rubbery at this stage." Before I could wrench free, kind hands thrust me into a topcoat, jammed an alien derby over my ears in the classic manner of Ben Welch, and

82

hustled me downstairs in a freight elevator. While
I kept trying to raise my head, which hung dahlia-
like on its stalk, the rescuers started wrangling
over my future.

"Take him home. . . . No, he'll cut himself. . . .
Who is he? . . . I know a spot where we can get
him some soup. . . . Yeah, soup's good." I gurgled
a feeble remonstrance that passed unnoticed; when
the dust blew away, I was propped up at a table
in a sleazy bar off the Gay White Way, staring
wanly into a bowl of buttermilk. My wife and her
grouping had disappeared and a noisy Syrian, rep-
resenting himself as the owner of a chain of shoe
stores in Hartford, was offering to take me into
partnership. Midway in his harangue, he broke
off and, hailing the bartender as "Four Eyes,"
ordered him to serve me a highball. The gibe evi-
dently climaxed a long, hard day for the bartender. With a hoarse bellow, he hurdled the
beerpulls and uncorked a left hook that I inter-
cepted nimbly with my ear. The Syrian thereupon lashed out handily and in a moment I was
bobbing between them like a cork. The estimate
is, of course, unofficial, but sports writers have

83

since estimated that I stopped more punches than Jacob "Soldier" Bartfield in his entire career.

I came to in an alley with two handsome shiners suitable for framing and the Hall Johnson Choir singing *Stabat Mater* inside my head. My wife had mysteriously reappeared and, aided by a shrill young couple, whose dialogue had been written for them by Clyde Fitch, was sponging me off. "Now take it easy, will you?" she implored, brushing back my widow's peak. "Everything is going to be all right. Just relax." I closed my eyes with a grateful sigh. When I opened them again, I was lying on a banquette in a clip joint off Amsterdam Avenue. Dawn was peeping in at the window and a spurious gypsy violinist was rendering gems from *The Bohemian Girl*. At the next table, a gaunt trio resembling Picasso's *The Absinthe Drinker*, dimly identifiable as my wife and the Fitches, was sobbing brokenly for Alt Wien. I stumbled to my feet, flung my last bit of collateral at the management, and, herding the revellers before me, started toward the door. Right outside it stood two monumental Texans fourteen feet high, with snow on their hair, clamoring for admission.

The ensuing action is somewhat hazy, but as I reconstruct it, our Mr. Fitch curtly bade Gog and Magog step aside, employing the informal phrase "you big crackers." I was scudding across the sidewalk, primly keeping my nose clean and my lips buttoned, when I abruptly felt myself seized by the collar and hoisted four feet into the air.

"What did you call me, you little measle?" one of the ogres was rumbling. "Why, I'll flatten that bugle—" He drew back a fist no larger than a peanut-fed ham; the breeze from the gesture alone dizzied me. I croaked out a pitiable denial and he let me drop. The fall nearly broke my ankles. In that instant, as I slunk after my party, I reached the most vital decision of my life. Three times in one evening I had pursed my lips against the grape and thrice my life had hung in the balance. Come hell or high water, famine, flood, or fire, I was through with milk and large moral resolutions. From here in, it's high carnival and strange purple sins. Bring me another pair of those amber witches, waiter, and go easy on the club soda.

PHYSICIAN, STEEL
THYSELF

Do YOU happen to know how many tassels a Restoration coxcomb wore at the knee? Or the kind of chafing dish a bunch of Skidmore girls would have used in a dormitory revel in 1911? Or the exact method of quarrying peat out of a bog at the time of the Irish Corn Laws? In fact, do you know anything at all that nobody else knows or, for that matter, gives a damn about? If you do, then sit tight, because one of these days you're going to Hollywood as a technical supervisor on a million-dollar movie. You may be a bore to your own family, but you're worth your weight in piastres to the picture business.

Yes, Hollywood dearly loves a technical expert,

however recondite or esoteric his field. It is a pretty picayune film that cannot afford at least one of them; sometimes they well-nigh outnumber the actors. The Sherlock Holmes series, for instance, employs three servants on a full-time basis—one who has made a lifelong study of the décor at 221-B Baker Street, a second deeply versed in the great detective's psychology and mannerisms, and a third who spots anachronisms in the script which may distress Holmesians, like penicillin and the atomic bomb. An ideal existence, you might think, and yet there have been exceptions. I knew a White Russian artillery officer at M-G-M, imported at bloodcurdling expense from Algeria as adviser on a romance of the Foreign Legion, who languished for two years in an oubliette under the Music Department. Over the noon yoghurt, his voice trembled as he spoke of his yearning to return to Russia, where they were waiting to shoot him, but the director of "Blistered Bugles" felt him indispensable. At last he departed, with close to forty thousand rutabagas in his money belt, a broken man. His sole contribution was that he had succeeded in having "*pouf*" altered to "*sacré bloo.*" Another expert I met during the same epoch was a jovial, gnarled little party named Settembrini, conceded to be the foremost wrought-iron craftsman in the country. He had been flown three thousand miles to authenticate several flambeaux shown briefly in a night shot of Versailles. We subsequently chanced to be on the same train going East, and except for the fact that he wore a gold derby and was lighting his cigar with a first-mortgage bond, he seemed untouched. "Fine place," he commented, flicking ashes into the corsage of a blonde he had brought along for the purpose. "Sunshine, pretty girls, grapefruit ten for a quarter." I asked him whether the flambeaux had met the test. "One hundred per cent," he replied, "but they threw 'em out. In the scene where Marie Antoinette comes down the steps, a lackey holds a flashlight so she don't trip over her feet."

The latest group of specialists to be smiled upon by the cinema industry, it would appear, are the psychoanalysts. The vogue of psychological films started by *Lady in the Dark* has resulted in flush times for the profession, and anyone who can tell

89

a frazzled id from a father fixation had better be booted and spurred for an impending summons to the Coast. The credit title of *Spellbound*, Alfred Hitchcock's recent thriller, for example, carried the acknowledgment "Psychiatric sequences supervised by Dr. May Romm," and Sidney Skolsky, reporting on a picture called *Obsessed* (formerly *One Man's Secret* and before that *One Woman's Secret*), states, "Joan Crawford is huddling with an eminent psychiatrist who will psych her forthcoming role in *The Secret* for her." A psychiatrist suddenly pitchforked into Hollywood, the ultimate nightmare, must feel rather like a small boy let loose in a toy store, but I wonder how long he can maintain a spirit of strict scientific objectivity. The ensuing vignette, a hasty attempt to adumbrate this new trend, is purely fanciful. There are, naturally, no such places as the Brown Derby, Vine Street, and Hollywood Boulevard, and if there should turn out to be, I couldn't be sorrier.

SHERMAN WORMSER, M.D., PHD., came out of the Hollywood Plaza Hotel, somewhat lethargic

after a heavy Sunday brunch, and paused inde-
cisively on the sidewalk. The idea of taking a walk,
which had seemed so inspired a moment ago in
his room, now depressed him immeasurably. To
the south, Vine Street stretched away intermin-
ably—unending blocks of bankrupt night clubs,
used-car lots, open-air markets, and bazaars full
of unpainted furniture and garden pottery. To
the north, it rose abruptly in a steep hill crowned
by a cluster of funeral homes and massage parlors
in tan stucco. Over all of it hung a warm miasma
vaguely suggestive of a steam laundry. Sherman
moved aimlessly toward the boulevard and paused
for a brief self-inventory in the window of the
Broadway-Hollywood department store.

Most of Dr. Wormser's patients in New York,
accustomed to his neat morning coat and pencil-
striped trousers, would have had some difficulty
in recognizing their father confessor at the moment. He wore a pea-green play suit with deep,
flaring lapels, tailored of rough, towel-like ma-
terial, arbitrarily checked and striated in front but
mysteriously turned to suède in back. Over a
gauzy, salmon-colored polo shirt he had knotted
a yellow foulard handkerchief in a bow reminis-

91

cent of George Primrose's Minstrels, and on his head was sportily perched an Alpinist's hat modelled after those worn by the tyrant Gessler. Eight weeks before, when he had arrived to check on the dream sequences of R.K.O.'s *Befuddled*, he would not have been caught dead in these vestments, but his sack suits had seemed so conspicuous that, chameleon-like, he soon developed a sense of protective coloration.

He had settled his hat at a jauntier angle and was turning away from the window when he became aware that a passer-by was staring fixedly at him. The man wore an off-white polo coat which hung open, its belt trailing on the pavement. Underneath were visible pleated lavender slacks and a monogrammed yachting jacket trimmed with brass buttons. The face under the scarlet beret was oddly familiar.

"I beg pardon," hesitated the stranger, "I think we—you're not Sherman Wormser, are you?" At the sound of his voice, Sherman's mouth opened in delight. He flung his arm about the man's shoulder's.

"Why Randy Kalbfus, you old son of a gun!"

92

he crowed. "Two years ago! The Mental Hygiene Convention in Cleveland!"

"Bull's-eye," chuckled Kalbfus. "I thought it was you, but—well, you look different, somehow."

"Why—er—I used to have a Vandyke." Wormser felt his cheeks growing pink. "I shaved it off out here. The studio, you know. Say, you had one, too, for that matter. What became of yours?"

"Same thing," Kalbfus admitted sheepishly. "My producer said it was corny. He's got a block about psychiatrists' wearing goatees."

"Yes, involuntary goatee rejection," nodded Wormser. "Stekel speaks of it. Well, well. I heard you were in town. Where you working?"

"Over at Twentieth. I'm straightening out a couple of traumas in *Delirious*."

"You don't say!" Despite himself, Sherman's tone was faintly patronizing. "I turned down that assignment, you know. Didn't feel I could justify the symbolism of the scene where Don Ameche disembowels the horse."

"Oh, that's all out now," said Kalbfus amiably. "That was the early version."

93

"Well," said Sherman quickly, eager to retrieve himself, "it's the early version that catches the Wormser, what?" Kalbfus laughed uproariously, less at the witticism than because this was the first time anyone had addressed him in three days.

"Look," he suggested, linking arms with Sherman, "let's hop over to the Bamboo Room and have a couple of Zombolas." On their way across to the Brown Derby, he explained the nature of the drink to Wormser, who was still a bit staid and Eastern in his choice of beverages. "It's just a tall glass of rum mixed with a jigger of gin, some camphor ice, and a twist of avocado," he said reassuringly.

"Isn't that a little potent?" asked Wormser dubiously.

"You're cooking with grass it's potent," returned his companion pertly, if inaccurately. "That's why they won't serve more than six to a customer." Seated in the cool darkness of the bar, with three Zombolas coursing through their vitals, the colleagues felt drawn to each other. No trace of professional hostility or envy lingered by the

94

time they had finished reviewing the Cleveland convention, the rapacity of their fellow-practitioners, and their own staunch integrity.

"How do you like it out here, Randy?" Wormser inquired. "I get a slight sense of confusion. Perhaps I'm not adjusted yet."

"You're inhibited," said Kalbfus, signalling the waiter to repeat. "You won't let yourself go. Infantile denial of your environment."

"I know," said Wormser plaintively, "but a few weeks ago I saw Jack Benny in a sleigh on Sunset Boulevard—with real reindeer. And last night an old hermit in a pillowcase stopped me and claimed the world was coming to an end. When I objected, he sold me a box of figs."

"You'll get used to it," the other replied. "I've been here five months, and to me it's God country. I never eat oranges, but hell, can you imagine three dozen for a quarter?"

"I guess you're right," admitted Wormser. "Where are you staying?"

"At the Sunburst Auto Motel on Cahuenga," said Kalbfus, draining his glass. "I'm sharing a room with two extra girls from Paramount."

95

"Oh, I'm sorry. I—I didn't know you and Mrs. Kalbfus were separated."

"Don't be archaic. She's living there, too." Kalbfus snapped his fingers at the waiter. "Once in a while I fall into the wrong bed, but Beryl's made her emotional readjustment; she's carrying on with a Greek in Malibu. Interesting sublimation of libido under stress, isn't it? I'm doing a paper on it." Wormser raised his hand ineffectually to ward off the fifth Zombola, but Kalbfus would not be overborne.

"None of that," he said sharply. "Come on, drink up. Yes, sir, it's a great town, but I'll tell you something, Sherm. We're in the wrong end of this business. Original stories—that's the caper." He looked around and lowered his voice. "I'll let you in on a secret, if you promise not to blab. I've been collaborating with the head barber over at Fox, and we've got a ten-strike. It's about a simple, unaffected manicurist who inherits fifty million smackers."

"A fantasy, eh?" Wormser pondered. "That's a good idea."

"What the hell do you mean, fantasy?" de-

96

manded Kalbfus heatedly. "It happens every day.
Wait till you hear the twisteroo, though. This
babe, who has everything—houses, yachts, cars,
three men in love with her—suddenly turns
around and gives back the dough."

"Why?" asked Wormser, sensing that he was
expected to.

"Well, we haven't worked that out yet," said
Kalbfus confidentially. "Probably a subconscious
wealth phobia. Anyway, Zanuck's offered us a
hundred and thirty G's for it, and it isn't even on
paper."

"Holy cow!" breathed Wormser. "What'll you
do with all that money?"

"I've got my eye on a place in Beverly," Kalbfus
confessed. "It's only eighteen rooms, but a jewel
box—indoor plunge, indoor rifle range, the whole
place is indoors. Even the barbecue."

"That can't be," protested Wormser. "The barbecue's always outdoors."

"Not this one," beamed Kalbfus. "That's what
makes it so unusual. Then, of course, I'll have to
give Beryl her settlement when the divorce comes
through."

"You—you just said everything was fine between you," faltered Wormser.

"Oh, sure, but I've really outgrown her," shrugged Kalbfus. "Listen, old man, I wouldn't want this to get into the columns. You see, I'm going to marry Ingrid Bergmann."

A strange, tingling numbness, like that induced by novocain, spread downward from the tips of Wormser's ears. "I didn't know you knew her," he murmured.

"I don't," said Kalbfus, "but I saw her the other night at the Mocambo, and she gave me a look that meant only one thing." He laughed and swallowed his sixth Zombola. "It's understandable, in a way. She must have known instinctively."

"Known what?" Wormser's eyes, trained to withstand the unusual, stood out in high relief.

"Oh, just that I happen to be the strongest man in the world," said Kalbfus modestly. He rose, drew a deep breath, and picked up the table. "Watch," he ordered, and flung it crisply across the bar. Two pyramids of bottles dissolved and crashed to the floor, taking with them a Filipino bus-boy and several hundred cocktail glasses. Before the fixtures had ceased quivering, a task force of bartenders and waiters was spearing down on Kalbfus. There was an obscure interval of scuffling, during which Wormser unaccountably found himself creeping about on all fours and being kicked by a fat lady. Then the shouts and recriminations blurred, and suddenly he felt the harsh impact of the pavement. In a parking lot, eons later, the mist cleared and he was seated on the running board of a sedan, palpating a robin's egg on his jaw. Kalbfus, his face puffier than he last remembered it, was shakily imploring him to forgive and dine at his motel. Wormser slowly shook his head.

"No, thanks." Though his tongue was a bolt of flannel, Sherman strove to give his words dignity. "I like you, Kalbfuth, but you're a little unthtable." Then he got to his feet, bowed formally, and went into the Pig'n Whistle for an atomburger and a frosted mango.

WHATEVER
GOES UP

WHEN it was announced a few days ago in *Variety* that a new musical comedy named *What's Up?*, dealing with the misadventures of some aviators whose plane is grounded near a girls' school, was cooling on top of the oven, Broadway's reaction was not slow in coming. "That's for me," observed one astute old showman with whom I was lunching at Lindy's. "I'll take a piece of that." The moment the waiter had brought him the strudel, however, he seemed less certain. "I don't know," he hesitated, trying to ingest the strudel without removing his toothpick and cigar. "It's a kind of a sophisticated idea. The public don't want to think—they want to laugh. Look at Chekhov."

We looked at Chekhov, who had just come in and was having a rolled-beef sandwich and a bottle of Dr. Brown's Celery Tonic in the corner. I got up and went over to his table.

"Hello, Chekhov," I said.

"Hello," he said.

"What happened to *you* last night?" I said.

"Brett and I waited for you at the Dingo," he said. Good old Chekhov. I could see him looking at the *Variety* in my pocket.

"Well, I guess you know," I said.

"Sure," he said. "Sure. I know."

"I suppose it had to happen," I said.

"Not that way it didn't," he said. "Not that way, old man. When I wrote *Uncle Vanya* none of *my* aviators were grounded near a girls' school."

"You didn't have any aviators in *Uncle Vanya*," I said.

"You bet I didn't," he said. "That's the point." He ordered another celery tonic.

"Better ease off, Chekhov," I said. "That makes four."

"I'm all right," he said cheerfully. That's one thing about Chekhov. No matter how many Dr.

102

Browns he's had, he never shows it. "Mind if I file some cables?" He drew some cables from his pocket and started filing them. I went back to my table and told my friend what he had said.

"Certainly," he nodded. "It ain't believable, aviators mixed up in a girls' school. Listen," he said confidentially, impaling a sour tomato on his index finger, "do you want to know what an astute old showman like I would do with that plot? I'd make them a bunch of girl aviators which they fall down near a boys' school. Paste that in your hat and smoke it."

I have been smoking it ever since last Tuesday and have arrived at the same conclusion. The basic idea of *What's Up?* is a dilly, but unless it is handled with extreme delicacy it may very well curdle. In the following libretto, I have taken the liberty of indicating one of the directions in which the story might go. There is still another, but I doubt whether the authors could be influenced to accept it at this point.

[*Scene 1: The cockpit of a fast monoplane high above the clouds. At rise, three fair aeronauts are*

103

discovered in white sateen uniforms with cute fur-trimmed collars and goggles: Phyllis Brontislaw, a gorgeous blonde; Valuta Imbrie, a gorgeous brunette; and Punkins Janeway, a gorgeous redhead. Valuta has just finished washing her luxuriant tresses and, while Phyllis busies herself steering their frail craft, spreads her crowning glory out to dry in the rays of the late-afternoon sun. Punkins, curled up on a sofa, is gorging herself on Tango Kisses and devouring the latest Donn Byrne novel.]

VALUTA: Well, here we are in the trackless empyrean, where every prospect pleases and only man is vile.

PHYLLIS: Men, men, men—can't you think of anything else?

PHYLLIS (*solo*):

"Men, Men, Men"
Oh, maidens fair, beware,
And likewise have a care,
Lest passion's kiss betrays
And lose you in a maze.

Men, men, men,
They're quite outside our ken,
Their ways are very devious,
It's lovey-us and leavey-us,
Men, men, men.

PUNKINS: Why so pensive, Val?

VALUTA: That's for me to know and you to find out.

PHYLLIS: Stuff and double stuff! All the world is aware that your aunt, Mrs. Morris Fenchurch of Shaker Heights and Piping Rock, made me take you along on my transcontinental dash to nip your budding romance with Señor Ramón Mulcahy, the Argentinian polo flash that has been turning feminine heads this season!

VALUTA (*hotly*): I'll have you know I'm in love with Ramón and propose to marry him!

PHYLLIS: We shall see what we shall see.

PUNKINS: Oh, stop scrapping, you two! Say, Phyl, what time are we due in Bethesda, Maryland?

PHYLLIS: Unless my eyes are playing me false, I believe I descry her environs now. *Oh!*

PUNKINS: What's the matter?

PHYLLIS: The engine's missing!

PUNKINS (*innocently*): Then how did we ever get this far?

PHYLLIS (*impatiently*): Something has gone wrong with the mechanism, silly. (*Thoughtfully*) Doubtless one of those little wheels inside is stuck.

105

VALUTA: Then it behooves us to "bail off" apace, lest we dash out our brains in the ensuing holocaust. Parachutes at the ready! (*Galvanized into action, the three pull their ripcords and float gently to earth. Midway they are joined by the ladies of the ensemble, forming a stunning aerial ballet which should leave the critics breathless in their seats. Note: This may be a bit difficult to stage, as the plane is resting on two sawhorses and the parachutes are bound to create hell's own tangle, but it can all be cut out on the road.*)

[*Scene 2: A dormitory room at Peachpit Military Academy. At rise, Perry Yeast, president of the senior class, is stretched disconsolately on a window seat, staring at the ceiling. His adoring henchman, "Skinny" Beaumarchais, whose bulk belies his sobriquet, surveys him with a look of anxiety on his rubicund physiognomy.*]

PERRY: Well, here we are on the eve of the annual Senior Hop and every girl at Miss Breitigam's sequestered with botulism resulting from sub-standard tinned meats. What to do?

SKINNY (*struck by an inspiration*): I've got it,

Chief! Why not charter a speedboat and run down to Montevideo, fabled for its feminine pulchritude?

SKINNY (*comic rumba*):

We'll throw a party with the señoritas lively,
There'll be rum and gourds and castanets, so drive me
To that cluster of palmettos and cabañas,
Where the mangoes are so fine, and the bananas. Etc.

PERRY: That's all very well, but the dance is scheduled to begin in half an hour, and if crusty Dean Vogelsang discovers we have no girls he will call it off, thereby making us a laughing stock.

SKINNY: It looks like we're sunk, unless some girls drop out of the sky. (*A knock at the door; enter Phyllis, Valuta, and Punkins, scantily clad.*)

PHYLLIS: Quick—hide us!

PERRY (*curiously*): What's the matter?

PHYLLIS: Crochety, near-sighted Dean Vogelsang's suspicions are aroused! There he is on the staircase now!

PERRY: What's your name?

PHYLLIS: Phyllis Brontislaw.

PERRY: That's the most beautiful name I've ever heard.

107

PERRY and PHYLLIS (*duet*):

A man and a maid were strolling
In some grass that was covered with dew,
When he took her hand and boldly pledged,
"I'll e'er remember you.
Come place your ruby lips on mine,
And love is all too fleeting,
We're here where journeys always end,
I.e., in lovers' meeting."

[*Skinny hastily pushes the girls into a closet;
enter Dean Vogelsang.*]

DEAN (*sternly*): Did I see three chickens run
in here a minute ago?

PERRY: No, and you're a near-sighted old fossil.

DEAN (*adjusting his ear trumpet*): What's that?
What's that?

PERRY: I said you sing as sweet as a throstle.

DEAN (*placated*): Well, that's different. Now
mind you, Yeast, you have ten minutes to find
partners for the Senior Hop or it's off.

PERRY (*deliberately*): I think . . . I may have
. . . a surprise for you, Dean Vogelsang.

[*Scene 3: The school auditorium, that evening.
Gay lanterns have transformed it into a veritable
fairyland, and a three-piece combination consist-*

108

ing of Zinkeiser (piano), Hildebrand (drums), and Calvosa (alto sax) is dispensing torrid rhythm. As laughing couples swirl by in the background, Skinny enters to the punchbowl at right, attended by his faithful henchman, "Happy" Telekian, whose mournful visage gainsays his nickname.]

HAPPY: Well, everybody is having loads of fun tonight, thanks to Perry's resourcefulness, but what are you putting in the punchbowl, Skinny?

SKINNY: Don't you catch on, stupid? It's our only chance. If Dean Vogelsang gets tipsy, he may not decide to flunk Perry in his forthcoming histology quiz, thus enabling us to beat Meatcliff and win the track crown at the conference.

HAPPY (*tensely*): We've only minutes to spare! (*The starter's pistol is heard off scene and the Meatcliff relay team flashes by on a treadmill at rear, a lap ahead of Peachpit. The crowd groans. Enter Punkins on Dean Vogelsang's arm.*)

PUNKINS (*flirtatiously*): Why, Vogie, you're a wonderful dancer—a regular Fred Astaire!

DEAN (*suspiciously*): What did you say about a chair?

PUNKINS: I said you were afraid to take a dare.

109

DEAN: Well, that's different. (*He drains a cup of punch, stifles a hiccough.*) Shay, girlie—hic—lesh you and I dansh.

PUNKINS (*craftily*): Will you let Perry run against Meatcliff? (*The crowd trembles on his decision.*)

DEAN: Yesh. (*He collapses in a drunken coma. As Perry doffs his "tux" and darts after the Meatcliff aggregation, the crowd goes wild with joy.*)

PHYLLIS: He's gaining!

VALUTA: Now he's at the turn! Now he's coming down the stretch! (*With a herculean effort, Perry breasts the tape and the rooters execute a frenzied snake dance to* Peachpit, Mother of Men.)

VALUTA (*nestling shyly in Perry's arms*): Well, thank goodness I got shut of that greaser Ramón in time to marry a clean-limbed American boy.

SKINNY (*to Mrs. Vetlugin, the house mother, who is extremely stout*): Well, I guess that's telling 'em, eh, fat lady? [*As Skinny and Happy pair off with Punkins and Valuta, the ensemble goes into a whirlwind finish, George Abbott goes into a passion, and the producers go into bankruptcy.*]

CURTAIN

110

PALE HANDS
I LOATHE

To paraphrase Omar the Tentmaker slightly (oh, come on, it can't hurt to paraphrase Omar the Tentmaker just a teeny bit), I often wonder what the editors of the *Woman's Home Companion* buy one half so precious as the thing they sell. The thing they sell me, specifically, is nepenthe; whenever my salt loses its savor, I know I can find heartsease in those shiny, optimistic pages, whether in the latest prize-winning recipe for macaroni-and-cheese timbales or some ingenious method of canning babies for winter use. More than a companion, yet less than a mistress, it is my home away from home, my wife away from wife, my dream girl of the magazine world. *Woman's Home Companion*, I adore you.

111

It was, therefore, with a sense of disquietude that I detected in the February issue a certain monotony I had never noticed before. The infants gurgled on as darling and cuddlesome as ever; the meat loaves and veal birds were, if anything, even more economical than they had been in the January number. But instead of the rich pastiche of lingerie and soufflés I expected in the advertising columns, I found only a series of variations on a single theme—the care of Milady's hands. For page after page, the manufacturers of innumerable unguents and lotions endlessly conjugated the tragedy of rough, chapped hands. "My poor hands!" snuffled the housewife in the advertisement for Pacquins Hand Cream. "They made me feel like an OLD TURKEY," and to dramatize the full poignancy of her affliction, the victim was shown in a second phase transmuted into an aged, weather-beaten turkey. "I use HINDS—that HONEY of a lotion," crowed another housewife, hefting a coal scuttle and celebrating you-know-whose Honey and Almond Cream. Jergens Lotion took a rather more romantic approach and portrayed a handsome officer nibbling at his fiancée's fingers,

112

while Campana Cream Balm presented a pair of war sweethearts over the hushed caption: "It was one of those golden, delirious moments . . . impulsively his hands sought mine . . . and together we welcomed the first tender touch of romance." Toushay, the "Beforehand" Lotion, demonstrated its versatility with four mysterious vignettes of a young lady stroking a kitten, washing her undies, simpering at some convalescent soldiers, and finally nuzzling her warrior, home on leave.

It was our humdrum old friend, Ivory Soap, though, that put its competitors to shame and set my ordinarily robust stomach palpitating like a plate of junket. It depicted a personable matron fondly discussing her mate over the telephone with some undisclosed critic, as follows: "Hardboiled? *Him?* Don't you believe it! What hardboiled husband would tramp halfway across town to get that special coffee cake I adore so for Sunday breakfast? Would a really tough guy take time out now and then—like in the middle of his favorite pecan pie—just to grab my hands and kiss them? Yes—gruff as he seems to others, in private he fairly *raves* about my pretty hands!"

113

I have searched diligently through Freud, Jung, Brill, Menninger, and Zilboorg for a clue to this interesting form of hand worship, but can find no analogous instance, either with or without pecans. I suspect, however, that if we pull on a pair of waders and whip the husband's stream of consciousness, using the kind of tackle Mr. Joyce employed on Leopold Bloom, we may catch a few shiners. Here, then, is the interior monologue of Lester Wagenhals, incisive, hard-bitten office manager of the Puissant Valve & Flange Corporation, as he sits at his desk about five o'clock of a midwinter afternoon:

"Funny taste in my mouth. Must be that noodle ring I had for lunch. Urr-r-gh. Good thing I keep extra bag of pecans in desk drawer. Careful now. Secretary might walk in. Nasty little snooper. Lovely hands, though. Wish I could bite them. Better not. Can't afford scandal. Just one quick bite? No. Complications. Lose my head. One bite leads to another. Road to hell paved with soft white hands. Good thought there. Wasting my time in business. Should have been poet. Plenty of mazuma in poetry if a man went at it efficiently. Snug studio in Greenwich Village. High

114

jinks. Red wine and red-hot mammas. Turn your damper down. Life in the old boy yet. Man is as young as he feels. Lick my weight in wildcats.

"Ought to finish this letter to Abernethy about those bushings. *Yours of the 14th inst. to hand.* There I go again. Hands all over the place. Try again. *Cannot see our way clear to take consignment off your hands.* No good. Sleep on it. Best not to rush into these things, anyway. Past five o'clock. Eunice waiting. Comb my hair and wash my. Steady. Lean against filing cabinet a second. Buzzing in the temples. Never should have eaten that noodle ring. Scores die as police blame poisoned noodle ring. FBI uncovers secret noodle ring in Midwest. Wait. Wipe perspiration off forehead. Reception clerk might blab to J.B. Can hear them talking right now. Wagenhals slowing up. Nice old duffer but can't keep abreast of modern methods. Organization full of dead ducks. Terminating as of the first. One month's salary in recognition of the service you have ren. Appreciate if you will explain system to Mr. Samish, the dirty sneak you have been protecting right in your own office. Law of the jungle, dog eat dog, root or die. Alert, capable executive desires wide-awake connection.

Sorry, position just filled. Sorry, looking for aggressive younger man. Will call you if anything. Compelled to foreclose. Beg to advise that insurance has lapsed. Some bank with facilities for handling smaller accounts like yours. Eunice taking in washing. Rough laundry hands. No more pecan pies. Bellevue. Oh, my God.

"Buck up now. Walk slowly past their desks. Bunch of clock-watchers. Lazy, no-good riffraff. Give them the old glare. Snap their heads off. Carlson at the water-cooler. O.K., Carlson, your goose is cooked. *Running Horse* sticking out of Bender's pocket. Knock them off tonight. No, tomorrow will do. Much too kindhearted for my own good.

"There. Lucky my getting this elevator car. Cute brunette, that operator. Pity she wears gloves. Bet she has superb hands. Ask her for a peek? No, might misunderstand. Invite her out for cocktail some time. Pretend I'm big advertising man. Need model with special type of fingers to pose for national account. Strictly business, no monkeyshines. Careful not to frighten her off. Discuss various types of hands. Purely scientific spirit. Index of character, they say. Yours, for example.

116

Cold hands, warm heart. Paternal smile, old enough to be your father. Casually mention wife. Hopeless invalid. Haven't had anything to do with her hands for years. Pile it on. Man needs pair of soft white hands to come home to. Home is where the hands are. Just the same, better use pseudonym. Never can tell about these dolls. Lead you on and then the shakedown. Man in Cleveland who fell for lady elevator starter. Turned out to be head of Midwest blackmail ring. Stripped him of his last noodle. Urr-r-gh. That taste again.

"Fresh air feels good. Where did I say meet Eunice? Astor? Plaza? No, Biltmore lobby. Walk along Sixth. Interesting shops around here. Secrets of the Polynesian Love Cults. Figure Drawing for Second-Year Sadists. Nice prints in this art store. French kid wearing porcelain casserole on head. Pretty racy if you could read the text. Plaster-of-Paris Venus. Ditto foot and hand. Chap who designed that never saw woman's hand. Do better with my eyes closed. Outrage the way they mulct unsuspecting public. Law against it. Letter to the *Times*. Couldn't palm it off on yours truly. Palm off hand. Neat phrase. Work it in.

"Green light. Cross now. Too late, catch it next
117

corner. Automat coming up. Just time for fast pecan bun before Eunice. No, mustn't. Sure to smell it on my breath. Use cloves. Only an evasion. Can't hurt to look in window, though. Row on row of delicious, crackly. Who's to tell? Never know when some friend of Eunice. Oh, rats. Only live once. Long time dead. Long time no pecan bun. Look up and down first. Hurry.

"Easy now. People looking at you. Stop trembling. Debonair stroll. Man of the world dropping in for late-afternoon snack. Nothing out of the ordinary. Draw hot chocolate first. Enough. Don't bother with saucer. Now the pastry. More pecans on the twist than the buns. Count them. Don't be a sheep. Get your money's worth. Look out, manager watching you. Three nickels, quickly. Something wrong. Door is stuck. Hit it. Pound it. There, it's opening. So is the panel in back. Woman's hand reaching through. Exquisite, tapering fingers redolent of Ivory Soap. One little kiss. Opportunity of a lifetime. Grab them, you fool! Yum yum yum yum yum. . . . Capital. Now all I have to do is talk my way out of this."

WHY BOYS
LEAVE HOME

Every woman worth her salt, and even the few unsalted ones I have known, cherishes somewhere in her heart midway between the auricle and the ventricle a lovely, pastel-tinted dream. Maid or matron, she longs to dress up her man in a velvet smoking jacket and red morocco slippers, plant him in his favorite easy chair with a pipe and a rattling good detective story, and then, the moment his eyes freeze over, launch into a catalogue of bargains available at the stores. My own chocolate drop is no exception. One evening a while ago, I tottered in from a grueling afternoon at the bookmaker's and collapsed heavily in my Morris chair. I barely had time to sluice my larynx with a healing emollient of honey, orange bitters and a drop of cognac to allay the insupportable sweetness before the nightly overture struck up.

"Well, I vum," began my helpmate, unfolding her newspaper. "Do you remember those cunning little doilies Sandra Vermifuge bought two years ago at Neiman & Marcus, in Dallas? She paid a dollar forty-nine for them, and here they are at McCreery's for only a dollar forty-three. I can't wait to see her face!"

"Neither can I," I giggled. "Let's call her up and tease her! Where does she live now?"

"In Spokane, I think," said my wife doubtfully. "But you don't really intend——"

"Why not?" I urged. "Oh, come on, it's only a twenty-three-dollar toll call!" My proposal was received with an icy silence that melted forty-five seconds later, just as I had relaxed my neck muscles and begun a realistic imitation of a transcontinental truck puffing up a grade.

"Macy's is holding its annual clearance of barbecue aprons," the Voice resumed. "We've got four, but I don't think you can have too many barbecue aprons, do you? . . . And look at this:

120

there's a sacrifice of poplin-covered steamer chairs at Altman's, eighty-nine dollars and ninety-eight cents, only twenty-two to a customer. . . . Genuine quilted-rayon cheese strainers, marked down to four fifty-four. . . . Now here's something we really need! . . . Are you awake?"

"Urg," I replied, to indicate I was drinking in every word.

"GIMBEL'S JACKS UP YOUR CAR!" she read breathlessly. "GIMBEL'S COVERS UP YOUR CAR. If you're going into the service or to Florida, leave your car protected, so it will stay spick-and-span until you return. Jack it up on our plywood jacks— they'll hold an eight-ton truck for the duration. Then cover it from stem to stern with our paper coverall to keep out dust, soot, grit and grime; it's sturdy kraft paper——"

"Listen!" I roared. "I like the car the way it is! I like it down there in the country with mushrooms in the clutch and chickens roosting in the glove compartment! And if you think I'm going to travel sixty-four miles in the dead of winter to dress up a '37 Plymouth in a paper tent, you can jolly well——"

"Of course not, gingerbread boy," agreed Circe

121

soothingly, "but it can't hurt if I stop in tomorrow and look at it, can it?"

Which may explain how I came to reel into the railroad station at Frogtown, New Jersey, yesterday morning in a sub-arctic dawn, my spectacles opaque with steam and my pygmy frame bent double under a massive carton. The freight agent squirted tobacco juice over my shoes in welcome.

"Back for the summer, eh?" he inquired. "Say, you certainly look awful. What are those big circles under your eyes?"

"Glasses," I said evenly. "What the hell do you think they are?"

"You never got 'em drinkin' milk," he guffawed, slapping his thigh. "Say, what's in that there box?"

"A body," I snapped. "The body of a freight agent with a long nose that he kept sticking into other people's business." There was a short, pregnant silence during which our eyes stood toe-to-toe and slugged it out. Then, humming a nonchalant air, I sauntered into a snowdrift outside and dawdled a scant hour and a half wondering how to cover the seven miles to my duchy without

122

a car. At last a friendly chicken farmer drew up, attracted by my humorous carrot nose, stovepipe hat and lumps of coal simulating buttons.

"Ain't no room up front here," he said hospitably, leaning out of the warm, cozy cab of his truck, "but you can ride back there with them pullets."

For the first couple of miles, it was a novel experience to travel with a boutonnière of Rhode Island Reds pecking at my cravat, but eventually their silly feminine chatter bored me, and averting my face, I drank in great healing lungfuls of the exhaust. With the perfect sense of timing that characterizes everything I do, I arranged matters so that my chariot was exactly abreast of the post office as a group of neighborhood louts emerged.

"Pretty good-sized capon you raised there, Zeb," they complimented my ferryman. "Figger on butcherin' him now or feedin' him through the winter?"

Their good-natured derision was infectious, and averting my face, I drank in great healing lungfuls of the pullets. Soon, however, the spires of my

123

château came into sight and I vaulted nimbly into a puddle, slashing a jagged rent in my overcoat, and trudged up the glare ice to Lackluster Farm. Time had wrought few changes in the old place; one or two chimneys had fallen down and passing sportsmen had blown out every pane of glass in the windows, but there was nothing amiss that fifty thousand dollars would not cure.

Divesting myself of my coat to insure a spanking case of pneumonia, I gamely caught up the carton and staggered to the barn where the car was housed. Fortunately, there was no need to waste time opening doors, as the wind had obligingly torn them from their tracks. The trip along the dark threshing floor was uneventful, except that I adroitly involved myself in a rope hanging from the beams and conceived the ridiculous notion that someone was trying to garrote me. I emitted a few piercing cries, however, and it shook itself loose. The car itself seemed more streamlined than I remembered it, until I realized that parties unknown had removed the tires, along with the wheels. I rarely give way to my feelings, but in the irritation of the moment, I gave those axles a kick

124

they will remember for many a day to come. As soon as my foot stopped throbbing, I routed out an old broom and transferred the dust and wheat chaff which had settled down over the body to my own. Then, arms akimbo, I shrewdly laid out my plan of campaign.

The first thing to do, I said to myself, was to get the car up on the wooden jacks. To accomplish this, I would need a stout tire jack, which must be in the luggage compartment. The key to the luggage compartment, though, was on my bureau sixty-four miles away, where I had prudently left it. Ergo, I must force the lock—child's play to one whose knowledge of mechanics was a household word for ten feet around. I procured a pinch bar from the toolroom, inserted it under the door of the luggage compartment, and heaved my weight downward as outlined in first-year physics.

After picking myself up from the floor, I twisted my handkerchief into a makeshift tourniquet and decided that the wooden jacks would be superfluous anyhow, as the car already stood staunchly on its transmission. The next step

125

hence, was to envelop it in the paper coverall. I clawed up the carton and eventually succeeded in setting up the coverall, though several times the wind sweeping through the barn bore me off into the fields like a box kite.

"Now, easy does it," I said cunningly—I had reached the stage where I was addressing myself aloud—and holding the coverall above my head like Paul and Virginia fleeing before the storm, I crept up over the top of the car and dropped it neatly into place. Unluckily, this left me pinned on my stomach in the dark, slowly throttling under sturdy kraft paper; and acting on a sudden obscure impulse, I decided not to linger. I went through the side of the coverall biting, gouging and scratching, and when I hit the lane, I kept on going. The natives are still talking about the meteor covered with chicken feathers that flashed across the Delaware River yesterday afternoon. And the minute he gets his breath back, the meteor's going to do a little talking himself—to Mrs. Meteor.

NO DEARTH OF MIRTH—
FILL OUT THE COUPON!

IF, ABOUT Christmas time, you notice me sporting a curious insignia on my vest, a stipple of small white spots as though I had been eating Royal Riviera pears with a spoon, it may interest you to know that you are looking at a full-fledged, bona-fide member of the original Fruit-of-the-Month Club. This is not to be confused with the Fruit-of-the-Loom Club, an organization I also belong to, which allows me to sleep an hour later than non-members, or the Fruit-of-the-Moola Club, a society that sells me United States currency at ten per cent off the list price. No, the Fruit-of-the-Month Club is a powerful and exclusive sodality originating at the Bear Creek Orchards in Med-

127

ford, Oregon, consecrated to supplying me and mine with Royal Riviera pears in December, grapefruit in January, apples in February, rare preserves in April, plums in June, summer pears in August, peaches in September, and Lavelle grapes in October. I became a member of this singular brotherhood quite by chance; a trifling favor I did a stranger earned his gratitude.

Late one afternoon several months ago I was seated at a rear table in Sardi's, browsing through *Billboard* over a cup of bohea, when a conversation near by arrested my attention. Two plausible characters in billycock hats, whose fly manner and diamond-paste stickpins stamped them theatrical promoters, were inveigling a defenseless old cotton converter into backing a costume drama.

"Why, it's as safe as houses," purred one of them. "Tell him the prologue again, Skins."

"Sure," agreed the individual addressed by that unsavory appellation. "We open in an Italian grotto back in the sixteenth century. That's on account of the public's crazy about the sixteenth century."

"Is that so?" inquired the converter. "I didn't know that."

"Just can't get enough of it," Skins assured him. "That's all they ask for in the ticket agencies—a good meaty show about the sixteenth century. Well, anyhow, our leading man is discovered in this grotto, writing on a parchment scroll with a feather. Pretty soon he sprinkles sand over the manuscript, pulls a bell rope, and his apprentice comes in. 'There, Giovanni, it's finished,' he says. 'Rush it to the printer.' 'What are you going to call it, Signor Boccaccio?' says the apprentice. '*The Decameron*,' says Boccaccio. 'It may be just a lot of smutty stories to you, but some day this here vellum will be immortal.' "

"Yes, that's very effective," said the converter thoughtfully. "And you say Charles Laughton's offered to play Boccaccio?"

"We've got him under wraps at the Hotel Edison," the first promoter replied smoothly. "He starts rehearsing the minute your check is dry. Here," he said, unscrewing a fountain pen. "Just make it out to Thimblerig Productions." My ire boiled over at their pettifoggery and, rising, I laid about me with the folded *Billboard* to such effect that the blackguards took to their heels, howling with pain. The victim, once I had exposed their

129

duplicity, was naturally all gratefulness—filled my case with cigars, offered to convert some cotton for me, besought me to share a home-cooked meal he had in his pocket. He finally gave me my liberty in exchange for my address, and a few days later a handsomely engraved certificate informed me that I had been proposed for and elected to the Fruit-of-the-Month Club.

It recently occurred to me while munching the alternate November selection, a rather mealy Winesap, that though there are countless kindred services designed to provide people with books, flowers, records, regional delicacies, and even diapers, no machinery has ever been devised to furnish them old jokes on a seasonal basis. "Would not the discerning," I asked myself, "welcome an association patterned after the Fruit-of-the-Month Club, purveying flavorful, old-fashioned gags— the kind of time-honored nifties Father used to make?" In my mind's eye, I envisioned thousands of subscribers to the Jape-of-the-Month Club receiving at specified intervals their hand-culled jokes packed in dry ice, suitable for use in domestic arguments, encounters with bill collectors, visits to

130

the dentist—in short, in all the trivial, everyday contingencies that recur throughout the year. Simultaneously, it struck me that the only person in America capable of grasping the magnitude of the scheme was Barnaby Chirp. Brilliant young publisher, writer, book reviewer, anthologist, columnist, and flaneur, Chirp had fathered many a compendium of hilarious rib-ticklers. His latest, *Laughing Gasp,* had sold six hundred and fifty thousand copies prior to publication; so well had it sold, in fact, that a first edition was never published. His motto, "Git thar fustest with the mustiest jokes," indubitably made him my man, and I rushed to his office to broach the idea. He jumped at it.

"It's the cat's pajamas—a peachamaroot!" he proclaimed, jumping at it. "Here, let me get this stuff out of the way so we can talk." Turning back to his desk, he delivered two radio broadcasts into a lapel microphone, organized a ten-cent-book cartel, wrote a thirty-five-thousand-word preface to *Higgledy-Piggledy: An Omnibus of Jocose Jugoslav Stories,* and sold the Scandinavian dramatic rights of *Laughing Gasp* to a small Dan-

131

ish producer in the bottom drawer. "Now then," he said, swinging toward me, "we'll fix the annual membership fee of the Jape-of-the-Month Club at twenty-five hundred a year."

"Isn't that a bit steep?" I asked.

"Not for people of discrimination, those who can afford the finer things," said Chirp. "We've got to winnow out the ragtag and bobtail. The next step is to find an impartial board of judges to choose our monthly wheezes. How about a publisher, a writer, a book reviewer, an anthologist, and a columnist?"

"Good notion," I said. "What say to a panel like this: Nelson Doubleday, MacKinley Kantor, Harry Hansen, Whit Burnett, and Louis Sobol?"

"Too diverse," he said. "They'd never get on. I'll tell you what—why don't we get one man who's *all* those things? Then there wouldn't be any silly squabbling."

"Listen," I said, "anyone who's all those things is a genius."

"Why, thank you," said Chirp, coloring with pleasure. "I like you, too. Of course, I don't know whether I can crowd the job into my schedule,

132

but I'll do my best. Now, exactly how would the Jape-of-the-Month function?"

"Well," I said, "during January and February we'd ship our subscribers good, pre-tested chestnuts about the weather. For example, if someone complains to you of the cold, you advise him to go to Mexico. He naturally asks why. 'Because,' you tell him, 'down there it's chili today and hot tamale.' "

"Fan my brow," giggled Chirp, scribbling a note on a pad. "That's a sockdolager! Mind if I use it in my column?"

"Not at all," I said. "That's where I read it last week. In July and August, applying the same principle, we mail our members warm-weather rejoinders. Suppose you're asked whether it's hot enough for you. 'Hot?' you say. 'It's so hot I feed my chickens cracked ice to keep 'em from laying hard-boiled eggs!' "

"I've heard that one somewhere before," muttered Chirp dubiously. "Ah, what the hell, I can always credit it to Dorothy Parker. What sort of jokes could we guarantee the rest of the year?"

"Whatever the occasion demands," I answered.

133

"In April, when your wife's mother generally pays a visit, we send out our Easter special. 'They ought to call our car a mother-in-law model,' you tell your wife. 'Why is that?' she asks. 'Because it's got a crank in the back seat.' Along about June, after your son's home from college, you'd say to your friends, 'Yes, Willie's got his B.A. and his M.A., but his P.A. still supports him.' See how it works?"

"Aha," said Chirp, "and I'll tell you what's wrong with it. It's too sophisticated for the average person. You've got to hoke it up."

"How do you mean?"

"Well, take that January selection. I'd change it to 'Down in Mexico it's chilly today and hot tomorrow.' "

"But what becomes of the point?" I asked.

"The point, the point!" bawled Chirp. "Everybody's always griping about the point! How do you think I'd fill my column every week if all the stories had to have a point?"

"You win," I yielded. "After all, you've got your finger on the popular pulse."

"Right," he said. "I find that if you leave the

134

nub out of your anecdotes once in a while, it intrigues the reader enormously. Here, look at the response I got on last week's column." He opened a drawer, took out a response, and showed it to me. Then he leaned back and gave me the dazzling smile with which he ushers in any discussion involving money. "O.K., son, how do we set this thing up?"

"Well," I said haltingly, "I suppose that since I thought of it—"

"Precisely," he finished. "You're certainly entitled to a share of the profits." He drew a pie chart on his pad, snipped out a minute wedge with a pair of scissors, and handed it to me. "There's your cut," he explained. "The rest goes into advertising, research, judges' fees, stuff like that. Can you wrap bundles?"

"Gee," I protested, "I saw myself in more of an executive role."

"Oh, a white-collar snob, eh?" sneered Chirp. "What are you afraid of—soiling your hands? I expect you to get out and do some canvassing, too. Ever been a salesman?"

"No," I said, stealthily reaching for my hat,

135

"but I heard a pip of a quip about one yesterday."

"You did?" Chirp caught up his pencil, his eyes gleaming.

"Yes," I said. "It seems that a salesman called Moss Hart stopped at a Bucks County farmhouse one night. The farmer's daughter, who was named Dorothy Parker, asked what his profession was. 'I'm a travelling man,' he said. 'Yes,' she riposted, 'I can see that by the bags under your eyes.'" As Chirp rocked back in his chair, helpless with laughter, I silently stole out the door. I left behind a pair of arctics, a solid gold briefcase, and a little portion of my reason, but I don't really care. Who would, with that kind of money coming in like clockwork every month?

TAKE TWO PARTS SAND,
ONE PART GIRL, AND STIR

Outside of the three Rs—the razor, the rope, and the revolver—I know only one sure-fire method of coping with the simmering heat we may cheerfully expect in this meridian from now to Labor Day. Whenever the mercury starts inching up the column, I take to the horizontal plane with a glass graduate trimmed with ferns, place a pinch of digitalis or any good heart stimulant at my elbow, and flip open the advertising section of *Vogue*. Fifteen minutes of that paradisaical prose, those dizzying non sequiturs, and my lips are as blue as Lake Louise. If you want a mackerel iced or a sherbet frozen, just bring it up and let me read the advertising section of *Vogue* over it. I

137

can also take care of small picnic parties up to five. The next time you're hot and breathless, remember the name, folks: Little Labrador Chilling & Dismaying Corporation.

It would require precision instruments as yet undreamed of to decide whether *Vogue's* advertisements contain more moonbeams per linear inch than those of its competitors, but the June issue was certainly a serious contender for the ecstasy sweepstakes. There was, for instance, the vagary which portrayed a Revolutionary heroine setting fire to a field of grain with this caption: *"The Patriotism in Her Heart Burned Wheat Fields.* It took courage that day in October, 1777 for Catherine Schuyler to apply the torch to her husband's wheat fields so that food would not fall into the hands of the enemy. The flames that consumed the wheat fields on the Schuyler estate near Saratoga burned with no greater brightness than the patriotism in Catherine Schuyler's heart." Then, with a triple forward somersault that would have done credit to Alfredo Codona, the wizard of the trapeze, the copywriter vaulted giddily into an appeal to American women to

138

augment their loveliness with Avon Cosmetics. Somewhat breathless, I turned the page and beheld a handsome young air woman crouched on a wing of her plane. "Test Pilot—Size 10," read the text. "Nine thousand feet above the flying field, a Hellcat fighter plane screams down in the dark blur of a power dive. Holding the stick of this four-hundred-mile-an-hour ship is a small firm hand." The owner of the small firm hand, I shortly discovered in the verbal power dive that followed, is an enthusiastic patron of DuBarry Beauty Preparations. The transition in logic was so abrupt that it was only by opening my mouth and screaming briefly, a procedure I had observed in the movies, that I was able to keep my eardrums from bursting.

The most singular display of the advertiser's eternal lust for novelty, though, was a bold, full-color photograph of an olive-skinned beauty, buried up to her corsage in sand, in the interests of Marvella Simulated Pearls. A matched string of the foregoing circled her voluptuous throat, and dimly visible in the background were a conch shell and a sponge, identifying the locale as the seaside. The model's face exhibited a resentment verging on ferocity, which was eminently pardonable; anybody mired in a quicksand, with only a string of simulated pearls to show for it, has a justifiable beef. And so have I. The connection between burning wheat field and cosmetic jar. Hellcat fighter and lipstick, is tenuous enough, God knows, but somehow the copywriter managed to link them with his sophistries. Why in Tophet a scowling nude stuck bolt upright in a sand bar should influence the reader to rush to his jeweller for a particular brand of artificial pearl, however, I cannot possibly imagine.

Perhaps if we reconstruct the circumstances under which this baffling campaign was conceived, a clue might be forthcoming. Let us, therefore, don a clean collar and sidle discreetly into the offices of Meeker, Cassavant, Singleton, Doubleday & Tripler, a fairly representative advertising agency.

[Scene: *The Brain Room of the agency, a conference chamber decorated in cerebral gray, Swedish modern furniture, and the inevitable van Gogh reproductions. As the curtain rises, Duckworth,*

*the copy chief, and four members of his staff—
Farish, Munkaczi, DeGroot, and Miss Drehdel—
are revealed plunged in thought.*]

DUCKWORTH (*impatiently*): Well, what do you
say, Farish? Got an angle, DeGroot?

FARISH: I still keep going back to my old idea,
V. J.

DUCKWORTH: What's that?

FARISH (*thirstily*): A good red-hot picture of a
dame in a transparent shimmy, with plenty of
thems and those (*suddenly conscious of Miss
Drehdel's presence*)—oh, excuse me.

MISS DREHDEL (*wearily*): That's all right. I
read Earl Wilson's column, too.

FARISH: And a balloon coming out of her
mouth saying, "I've had my Vita-Ray Cheese
Straws today—*have you?*"

DUCKWORTH: No-o-o, it doesn't—it doesn't
sing, if you know what I mean. I feel there's something gay and youthful and alive about these
cheese straws. That's the note I want to hear in
our copy.

DEGROOT: How about a gay, newborn baby in
a crib? That would include the various elements.

141

I'd like to see a line like "No harsh abrasives to upset tender tummies."

DUCKWORTH: No it's static. To me it lacks dynamism.

MISS DREHDEL: What's wrong with a closeup of the cheese straws and "20 cents a box" underneath?

DUCKWORTH: Over-simplification. They'd never get it.

MUNKACZI (violently): I've got it, V. J., *I've got it!*

DUCKWORTH: What?

MUNKACZI: We'll take one of these Conover models and bury her up to her neck in sand! Maybe some driftwood or a couple of clams for drama!

FARISH: How do we tie in the cheese straws?

MUNKACZI: I haven't worked it out yet, but it smells right to me.

DUCKWORTH (*excitedly*): Wait a minute, now —you threw me into something when you said "sand." What we need is grit—punch—conflict. I see a foxhole at Anzio—shells bursting—a doughboy with shining eyes saying, "This is

142

what I'm fighting for, Ma—freedom of purchase the American Way—the right to buy Vita-Ray Cheese Straws on every drug, grocery, and delicatessen counter from coast to coast!"

FARISH: Man, oh man, that's terrific! I'll buy that!

DEGROOT: It's poetic and yet it's timely, too! It's a blockbuster, V. J.!

DUCKWORTH (*radiant*): You really mean it? You're sure you're not telling me this just because I'm the boss? (*Indignation in varying degree from all*) O.K. If there's one thing I can't abide, it's a lot of yes men around me. Now let's get on to the Hush-a-Bye Blanket account. Any hunches?

DEGROOT: We got a darb. (*Producing two photographs*) This is what the nap of a Hush-a-Bye looks like under the microscope.

FARISH: And here's the average blanket. See the difference?

DUCKWORTH: Why, yes. It has twice as many woollen fibers as the Hush-a-Bye.

DEGROOT (*happily*): Check. There's our campaign.

143

DUCKWORTH: Hmm. Isn't that sort of defeatist?

FARISH: A little, but it shows we don't make extravagant claims.

DEGROOT: We could always switch the photographs.

FARISH: Sure, nobody ever looks at their blanket through a microscope.

DUCKWORTH (*dubiously*): We-e-ll, I don't know. I like your approach to the challenge, but I don't think you've extracted its— its thematic milk, shall I say. Now, I for one saw a different line of attack.

FARISH (*instantly*): Me too, V. J. What I visualize is a show girl with a real nifty chassis in a peekaboo nightgown. Here, I'll draw you a sketch—

MISS DREHDEL: Don't bother. We can read your mind.

MUNKACZI: Listen, V. J., do you want a wrinkle that'll revolutionize the business? Answer yes or no.

DUCKWORTH: Does it fit in with the product?

MUNKACZI: Fit in? It grows right out of it!

144

You're looking at a beach, see? Voom! Right in front of you is a Powers girl buried up to the bust in sand, with some horseshoe crabs or seaweed as an accent.

DUCKWORTH: Do you see a Hush-a-Bye blanket anywhere in the composition?

MUNKACZI: No, that would be hitting it on the nose. Indirection, V. J., that's the whole trend today.

DUCKWORTH: You've realized the problem, Munkaczi, but your synthesis is faulty. I miss a sense of scope. Who are we rooting for?

MUNKACZI: Well, of course I was only spitballing. I haven't had time to explore every cranny.

DUCKWORTH: Look, kids, if you don't like what I'm about to suggest, will you tell me?

FARISH (*fiercely*): I've never been a stooge for anyone yet.

DEGROOT: You said it. There's not enough money in the world to buy *my* vote.

DUCKWORTH: That's the stuff. I want guts in this organization, not a bunch of namby-pambies scared that I'll kick 'em out into the breadline. Now this is hazy, mind you, but it's all there. A beachhead in the Solomons—a plain, ordinary G. I. Joe in a slit trench, grinning at the consumer through the muck and grime on his face, and asking, "Are you backing me up with Hush-a-Bye Blankets at home? Gee, Mom, don't sabotage my birthright with sleazy, inferior brands!"

DeGroot: Holy cow, that'll tear their hearts out!

Farish (*with a sob*): It brings a lump to your throat. It's a portion of common everyday experience.

Duckworth: Remember, men, it isn't sacred. If you think you can improve the phrasing—

DeGroot: I wouldn't change a word of it.

Farish: It's got balance and flow and discipline. Say it again, will you, V. J.?

Duckworth: No, it's pretty near lunch and we still need a slant for the Marvella Pearl people.

Munkaczi (*exalted*): Your troubles are over, boss. I got something that leaps from the printed page into the hearts of a million women! It's four A.M. in the Aleutians. A haggard, unshaven Marine is kneeling in a shell hole, pointing his rifle at you and whispering, "Start thinking, sis-

146

ter! When Johnny comes marching home are you going to be poised and serene with Marvella Pearls or just another housewife?"

FARISH: Cripes, I had the same notion, V. J. He took the words right out of my mouth!

DeGROOT: I'll go for that! It's as timely as tomorrow's newspaper!

DUCKWORTH: There's only one thing wrong with it. It's *too* timely.

DeGROOT (*eagerly*): That's what I meant. It's depressing.

FARISH: It reminds people of their troubles. Ugh!

DUCKWORTH: Precisely. Now, I've been mulling a concept which is a trifle on the exotic side but fundamentally sound. Mark you, I'm merely talking out loud. A girl on a bathing beach, almost totally buried in the sand, with a Marvella necklace and a brooding, inscrutable expression like the Sphinx. Haunting but inviting—the eternal riddle of womankind.

DeGROOT (*emotionally*): V. J., do you want my candid opinion? I wouldn't tell this to my own mother, but you've just made advertising history!

FARISH: It's provocative, muscular, three-dimen-

147

sional! It's got a *spiral* quality, the more you think of it.

DUCKWORTH: How does it hit you, Munkaczi?

MUNKACZI (*warmly*): I couldn't like it more if it was my own idea.

DUCKWORTH: I wonder if Miss Drehdel can give us the woman's reaction, in a word.

MISS DREHDEL (*rising*): You bet I can. The word I'm thinking of rhymes with Sphinx. (*Sunnily*) Well, goodbye now. If anybody wants me, I'm over at Tim's, up to here in sawdust and Cuba Libres. (*She goes; a pause.*)

FARISH: I always said there was something sneaky about her.

DEGROOT: Women and business don't mix.

MUNKACZI: You can never tell what they're really thinking.

FARISH (*cackling*): Old V. J. smoked her out though, didn't he?

DUCKWORTH (*expansively*): Yes, I may be wrong, but this is one conference she won't forget in a hurry, eh, boys? (*As the boys chuckle loyally and scuffle to light his cigar*).

CURTAIN

NOTHIN' COULD BE FINER THAN TO DINE FROM MANNY'S CHINA IN THE MORNIN'

(A POWER DIVE INTO THE NEW JOURNALISM)

Once in every newspaper's life comes a time when it feels it should interview Tommy Manville. PM's time came when it was announced that Thomas Franklin, Jr., was going to take Darlene Marlowe as his eighth wife. We called one of our girls over, told her we couldn't recall that any paper had ever tried to explain why Tommy was that way or what he seriously sought in life. Would she see what could be done along those lines?

Starting with a clipping that said Tommy sometimes stayed at the Savoy-Plaza, our girl called there.

"No, dear," said the Savoy-Plaza operator, "he's not here. He hasn't been here in over a year."

Our girl sent out some telegrams, made a lot of phone calls to hotels and night clubs. The net result was a lot of reports the Manville-Marlowe romance was off.

Then our girl's phone rang. She answered it and heard: "This is good old Tommy Manville," in a man's voice that ended in a little low giggle.— *From a recent Sunday* PM.

[*Every once in a while a little fifteen-cent magazine like "The New Yorker" hears that some out-
of-town person or other has arrived in New York.
Being a little fifteen-cent magazine, we naturally
have sources of information, or "pipe lines," that
other folks don't. So when we heard that Manuel
Dexterides, who is supposed to know more about
Tommy Manville than Tommy Manville knows
about himself, was in town from the Coast, we
thought you'd like to know what Dexterides was
thinking these days. We called in one of our girls
and asked her to see what she could find out. She
said she would have loved doing it, but she was
having her nails done that day at Elizabeth Arden's ("The New Yorker" carries no advertising
it cannot get), and she hoped we would ask her
again soon. Her roommate happened to walk in
just then, so we asked her to take over, and this is
what she learned. We'll let her tell it in her own
words, because we believe they are pretty good
words for a Sarah Lawrence alumna, and because
they reflect what people are thinking and feeling
down here at "The New Yorker" office.*]

150

THE photographer and I started out one cold morning last week from the corner of Forty-fifth and Forty-sixth to find Mr. Dexterides. (The copy desk says Forty-fifth and Forty-sixth don't intersect, but ordinary people, the kind who bear their own children and rarely go to the Persian Room, don't look at things through the eyes of a copy desk.) We had some trouble figuring out how to get uptown, as that part of Manhattan is full of short streets running at different angles, so we decided not to look for Mr. Dexterides until the following day and went instead to Café Society Downtown to interview genial Barney Josephson, but he was out of town. The next morning I met the photographer at the Kiss Room of El Borracho, and we called the Sherry-Netherland to see if Mr. Dexterides was staying there. The operator sounded pretty suspicious, though she finally put us through. A woman's voice with a faint foreign accent answered. She got excited when we explained what we wanted.

"Use the towels in the hamper!" she cried. "You think I'm made of towels?" I jiggled the hook and asked the operator whether she had

151

given me the right connection. She rang off. I didn't need to be told twice what the policy of the Sherry-Netherland's management was toward *New Yorker* employees. We went round the corner to the Hamburger Hearth, had a cup of coffee you would have paid fifteen cents for at any de-luxe hotel, and talked it over. The photographer suggested we call up Celebrities Service, which tells you where prominent people are staying, but that seemed too uncomplicated. Eventually, after checking half a dozen columnists and Broadway tipsters, we picked up a rumor that Dexterides was registered under the name of Barney Zweifel at the Hotel Whitebait on Forty-fifth Street. A cold, tight voice told us to come over whenever we liked. We killed a little time to show we weren't too anxious, had a nickel cup of coffee in a drugstore that would have cost a dime in any hamburger joint, and headed for the Whitebait.

There were four men playing poker in Room 602, and the air was thick with some sort of tobacco smoke I couldn't identify. Then I noticed that all of them had curious brown cylinders

152

clamped in their teeth. I asked if these were cigars.

"You said it, dearie," one man told me. (I discovered later that terms of endearment like "darling" and "honey" are frequent in the colorful horse-racing patois of Times Square.) I said I'd been sent by *The New Yorker* to sound out Dexterides. A heavy-set man, kind of benevolent, yet sneaky in the way you remember your uncle, looked up quickly. His cigar fell out of his mouth. I could tell he was startled.

"You're Zweifel, aren't you?" He nodded. "The grapevine says Zweifel is Dexterides. That means you're Dexterides."

"It does, hey?" he asked cautiously, hugging his hand closer to him.

"You play your cards pretty close to your chest, don't you, Mr. Dexterides?" I said.

"It's the only way I can see them," he apologized. "I'm a very nearsighted man."

"Look," I said, taking the bull by the horns, "our readers want to get behind your façade. To them Dexterides is an enigma. What are you really like, underneath?"

153

"Scram, boys," said Dexterides briefly. Two of his friends rose and went out. The other went out without rising. Dexterides gave me a shy, pleasant smile that reminded me of a little boy, and indicated the photographer. "Do we need him too? It could be real clubby in here." I saw that the presence of a third person embarrassed him, and asked the photographer to wait in the corridor. Dexterides explained that the hotel had a rule prohibiting visitors from waiting in the corridor, and suggested that he wait in the lobby, or, better still, the *New Yorker* office. As soon as we were alone, Dexterides' air of reserve vanished. He mixed two ginger-ale highballs, adjusted the Venetian blind so the sun wouldn't shine in my eyes while I was writing, and seated himself on the davenport by me. I told him our readers wanted to know what he was thinking about Tommy Manville these days. He frowned.

"Hats off to that question," he said seriously. "It's a good one. I'd say Tommy is a man that is in the prime of life at the present time." His eyes twinkled. "Funny thing about age. Now, I place you about eighteen or a little younger."

154

"I'll be twenty-three in March."

"Then I'm in the clear," he said, with a deep, full-throated chuckle that was thoroughly infectious. You knew instinctively that this warm, friendly man enjoyed simple things and people, and still there was a wholesome faith, almost akin to idealism, about him. Somehow I saw him standing at the right hand of King John on the Field of the Cloth of Gold as the Magna Carta was being signed. I asked him to outline his personal philosophy.

"I believe the day is coming when it will be possible to tell a person's age from their hands," he said. "I've made a study of the subject over the last few years. Take yours, for instance." To illustrate his theory, he gently manipulated my fingers, showing how excessive writing causes fatigue and how the soft cup of the palm acts as a cushion.

"As a matter of fact," he went on, "a girl with your type hands shouldn't be engaged in your particular type work. You ought to have a little spot of your own, which you could stick around all afternoon there in merely a kimona and play with a little poodle or so."

"But Manny," I said (he had insisted we conduct the interview as informally as possible), "don't you think the American woman of today must take her place shoulder to shoulder with men?"

"Hats off to that spirit," endorsed Dexterides emphatically. "Shoulder to shoulder is my motto one hundred per cent. Here, babe, leave me throw that pillow out of the way so it don't distress your back." It was impossible, I said to myself, that I had met this kindly, considerate man only today; I felt we had known each other for years. His voice had a husky quality that was oddly appealing. "At the same time," he continued, "it behooves each and every one of you to make the most of theirself, so as to keep faith with the boys in the forward areas. Take your hair, now," he said thoughtfully. "Why do you wear it in a flat bun like that? Allow me." He took it down and draped it loosely over my shoulders. "And those moccasins," he went on, "they're stifling your feet. You never saw a wild animal wearing moccasins, did you? It's flying in the face of Nature." I removed them

156

and was amazed at the sense of liberation it gave me.

"If I may turn personal for a moment," I asked, "what reactions do you, as a public figure, have regarding women's clothes?"

"There you will think me a bit unconventional," laughed Dexterides. "I think they wear too many—that is, too many of the wrong kind," he added hastily. "You got to let your body breathe. It is my belief that young women today are deliberately strangling their form under layers of rayon and acetate, thus doing untold harm to future generations. Of course, I do not include garments with a bit of spice to them, such as those lacy black doodads, which I am personally very partial to them. I forget exactly what you call them." He poured a fourth highball and we tried to think of the word he meant. "I'll show you later," he offered. "I know a little specialty shop near by that stays open till nine." The mention of time recalled me to a sense of my responsibilities. I looked quickly at my wrist watch, but it was gone. So was my pad and pencil, and to make matters worse, I had completely forgotten to bring

157

along my press pass. For all Mr. Dexterides knew, I might have been any little tramp from across the hall, but it never made a particle of difference in his attitude.

Sitting here in the office and looking back over the rest of our interview, I don't recall much of general interest that happened after this point. Broadly speaking, I got the impression of a masterful, compelling personality governed by the maxim "If you don't see what you want, ask for it." Hats, shoes, and clothes off to Manuel Dexterides, a rugged, unaffected American and a generous host, a man whose single-mindedness of purpose takes your breath away and points toward the dawn of a new tomorrow.

THE CUSTOMER IS
ALWAYS WRONG

I DARESAY that one of the strangest contradic-
tions to beset contradiction fanciers recently was
the situation confronting anybody who was seeking shelter in New York City. Not only were hotel
rooms scarcer than hen's teeth—after all, you
could pick up an occasional hen's tooth before
Christmas if you didn't mind going into the black
market for it—but the reason for their scarcity
was that most of them were occupied by people
who had flocked to the National Hotel Exposition
to discuss the scarcity of hotel rooms. Sounds para-
doxical, doesn't it? I mean, if there aren't any
other paradoxes around.

The National Hotel Exposition, it seems, is an

annual powwow at which innkeepers forgather to discuss trade secrets: the maintenance of proper standards of insolence among room clerks, improved methods of juggling shower faucets so that guests are alternately frozen and parboiled, artful techniques for making windows stick, and the like. The chief topic of the convention, understandably, was overcrowding. A variety of speakers addressed the gathering, analyzing the congestion and suggesting remedies. The majority plumped for "good public relations" and similar shadowy panaceas, but one delegate from the City of Brotherly Love came out of his corner snarling. "The resident manager of the Warwick Hotel, in Philadelphia," stated the *Times*, "suggested a more selective method of meting out rooms ... declaring himself in favor of the 'prestige guest who will be a source of revenue to the hotel,' adding that many long-term guests who are 'meaningless people' were cluttering up hotels and preventing them from gaining good prospects." This acid diagnosis was challenged from the floor (I use the term in its parliamentary sense; I would not wish to imply the gentleman was under the table) by an official

of Chicago's Palmer House with the hot assertion
that "the unimportant guest of today may be the
'big shot of tomorrow.'" The *Times* did not
divulge the outcome of the spat, but I presume the
principals invoked the code duello and pelted each
other with Nesselrode pudding until the weaker
cried uncle.

It so happens that several days ago I was privileged to see the Chicagoan's philosophy dramat-
ically vindicated before my very eyes in the lobby
of the San Culotte, a rather dusty family hotel in
the West Forties. I had gone there to meet a friend
with whom I was lunching, Tom Pulsifer. Now
Pulsifer is a good fellow (as a matter of fact, he is
nothing of the sort; he is a mealy-mouthed sponger
and a sneak), but he is never less than a half-hour
late for appointments, and as I am invariably a
half-hour early, I had oodles of time. I consumed
a few by reading the *Sun* in its entirety, including
such stop-press items as the news that Luna moths
frequently attain a wing span of four inches and
that the scup, or porgy, feeds on plankton. I don't
know what it is about plankton that fascinates the
Sun's make-up editor; he would rather run a good

sparkling dispatch about plankton than the size of Nita Naldi's superstructure or some matter of genuine civic importance. Anyway, it set me wondering what Pulsifer, whose features are indistinguishable from those of a scup, would feed on, and borrowing a menu from a waiter, I worked out a series of light, nutritious salads and entrées I could gracefully direct to his attention. It was sheer boondoggling, I knew; he would inevitably start clamoring for canvas-back and muscat grapes, and I would have to live out the month on salt cod to foot the bill. I had worked myself up into a very respectable fury at Pulsifer's gluttony and was about to phone him to cadge a meal from somebody else when I heard an irate voice behind me.

"Look at this lobby!" it was saying. "Did you ever see such a pack of crumbs? Of all the inconsequential, meaningless loafers—" I stole a glance over my shoulder and beheld a pursy, apoplectic gentleman, unmistakably the manager, surveying the lounge with arms akimbo. He was addressing a lath-like subordinate in mournful black and rimless bifocals, quite obviously his assistant.

162

"Shh, Mr. Leftwich," the younger man placated. "They're all steady guests, except one or two. Been here for years."

"You bet they have," snapped his superior. "That's what's wrong with the San Culotte. I tell you, Rightwich, I've had enough of these measly nonentities lousing up my establishment. I want people that *mean* something—celebrities, d'ye hear? Diplomats, movie stars, suave men of letters!"

"We had a suave man of letters last summer," reminded Rightwich, "but he left on account of the roaches."

"Listen," grated the manager. "I put thirteen thousand dollars' worth of roaches into this place to give it a homelike atmosphere, and anybody who doesn't like 'em can start packing!" He moved into my line of vision and indicated a commonplace citizen sleepily engaged in paring his nails. "Now, take that chump, for instance," he went on in a lower voice. "Who is he?"

"That's Mr. Detweiler," replied Rightwich. "He's an ideal guest. Never missed a bill. Why, he's so prompt—"

163

"Never mind that," interrupted Leftwich. "Promptness don't get you into *Who's Who*. What's he *do*?"

"Well," hesitated Rightwich, "he just sort of grooms his nails."

"You see?" snorted the other, triumphantly. "Dead wood. What I want is Humphrey Bogart sitting there grooming his nails, not a cipher named Detweiler. How about the one with the *Racing Form*, by the potted palm?"

"Mr. Pfannkuchen?" protested Rightwich, aggrieved. "Ah, gee, boss, he's gilt-edged—he pays us a year in advance. And he doesn't even ask for a room. He sleeps in a broom closet."

"He's a bottleneck," grunted Leftwich inexorably. "The place is full of 'em. That old lady knitting the afghan there—"

"She's kind of distinguished, though," appealed the assistant. "She looks like Dame May Whitty if you close your eyes a little."

"I'm closing my ears, too," growled Leftwich. "Get this straight, now. We're combing the small fry out of the register once and for all. I'll have public personalities like Jerome Zerbe and Choo

Choo Johnson snoozing around this lobby or, by jiminy, I'll padlock the joint!"

"But gosh, Mr. Leftwich," implored the young man. "You can't tell, one of our guests *might* become famous all of a sudden. Every dog has his day."

"Just a minute," rapped the manager, wheeling on him. "Are you trying to take sides with the clientele?"

"No, no, of course not," stammered Rightwich, overcome with confusion. "All I mean is—"

"We've got an ugly name for that in our business, boy." Leftwich's eyes had narrowed to mere slits. "It's called taking sides with the clientele."

"You know I wouldn't do a thing like that, sir," Rightwich pleaded.

"Well, I'm not so sure," his superior said suspiciously. "You worked at the Palmer House in Chicago, I seem to recall. If I hear any of that vicious Socialist twaddle about treating guests like human beings—"

"That was before I had my nervous breakdown," confessed Rightwich. "Oh, I know they're a lot of numskulls, but perhaps they're lucky, too.

That girl sitting near the magazine stand with her mouth open might turn out to be another Jennifer Jones."

"She'd better work fast," retorted the manager, "because I'm going to screen the whole damn bunch right now. March 'em into the banquet room—and better pass out barrel staves to the help. They might turn nasty." Impervious to Rightwich's attempts to pacify him, Leftwich swung about and neatly caromed into a vital, incisive individual who had just entered the lobby. Before Leftwich could kick him, the newcomer whisked a briefcase from under his arm and unbuckled it.

"May I have your very kind attention for a moment, folks?" he asked in a ringing voice. The hum of chatter died away and heads turned inquisitively. Leftwich's dewlaps flushed scarlet.

"See here, Mac," he began. "We don't allow any pitchmen—"

"I beg your pardon," the stranger returned icily. "I'm Victor Robinette of Menafee, Soutache, Heppenstall & Preiselbeere, the advertising agency. Is there a Mr. Aubrey Detweiler here?"

166

"Why—er—yes," spoke up the dim man with the nail file. "That's me."

"Congrats, Mr. Detweiler!" boomed Robinette. "You've just been awarded first prize by the Invisible Mitten Corporation in their America's Most Expressive Hands Contest. Here is our check for ten thousand dollars." A spontaneous cheer burst from the throats of the assemblage, and well-wishers clustered about Detweiler, stroking his hands curiously and attempting to put the bite on him. Simultaneously, above the excited babble, the shrill pipe of a bellboy arrested the attention of all.

"Mr. Pfannkuchen, call for Mr. Dorian Pfannkuchen!" An overwrought lad in buttons threaded his way to the student of the *Racing Form*. "It's your bookmaker! You've won the daily double at Hialeah Park!"

"But the nags don't start running till three hours from now," objected Pfannkuchen, dumfounded.

"That's mere shilly-shallying," dismissed the boy, tumbling twenty-six thousand dollars in crisp greenbacks into his lap. "The fact remains that you are a veritable Monte Cristo, as sure as God made little green apples."

"Yes, and that's not all!" sang out Mrs. Roraback, the erstwhile anonymous knitter, jubilantly waving a money order in five figures. "A special-delivery screed from the Albright Gallery in Buffalo informs me that they consider my last afghan an outstanding example of American folk art! Commissions are pouring in like herrings," she beamed, displaying sizable advance orders for throws, coverlets, and foot warmers. As flashlight bulbs exploded and newsreel cameramen jostled each other for advantage, Leftwich stood rooted to the spot, boiling with frustration.

"Try and cross me, will they?" he panted. "I'll get the spiteful creatures out of here if I have to burn the building down!" But fresh surprises still lay in store for him; two Hollywood directors, complete with megaphones, white riding breeches, and reversed linen caps, had appeared and were closely scrutinizing the girl near the magazine stand.

"She's dynamite!" the first murmured, awestruck. "She's another Jennifer Jones!"

"You skimmed the words off my lips," assented the second. "I see her as Eppie in *Silas Marner*, or *The Mill on the Frost*."

"No, I see her more as the scheming quadroon in *Pudd'nhead Wilson*," his companion demurred.

"That's what I say," nodded the first. "She's versatile—she can play anything. Pact her!" In a trice, their discovery was signed to a seven-year contract, had had her hair restyled by Antoine, and, swathed in platina mink and orchids, was announcing her retirement from the screen to return to Broadway. Gloating unashamedly, Rightwich clapped his elder colleague on the back.

"Well, sir," he observed slyly, "this'll teach you not to go off half-cocked in future, ah?"

With a hoarse bellow, Leftwich struck his arm away. "I'll find *somebody* around here who's a no-account stooge!" he roared. His eyes darted about wildly and fastened on me. He extended an accusatory finger. "Who are you? What are you doing here?"

"Me? Why, nothing," I said automatically, and then caught myself at the indiscretion. "I—I

169

mean, I've got a couple of diamond mines in the Rand, but please, I loathe publicity—"

"I knew it!" crackled Leftwich. "He's the one who's been cluttering up the building. Grab him, men!" In vain to protest that I was no guest of the house; rude hands seized my coat collar and frog-marched me toward the manager's office. Then, at the darkest hour, dawned deliverance. Through the revolving doors swept Tom Pulsifer —a Pulsifer reborn, a new authority in his bearing.

"Stop!" he thundered. "That man is my friend. Year in, year out, he has paid for my lunches, even when it meant denying himself luxuries and subsisting on soup greens. Now, thanks to the untimely demise of a crusty uncle in Australia, I can make belated restitution." And despite my most vigorous protestations, he stuffed my pockets with wad on wad of large-denomination currency. The discomfiture on Leftwich's countenance was comical in the extreme. Deferential to the point of servility, he fawned on us.

"Won't you stay and have lunch in my suite, gents?" he begged silkily. "I've a bottle of mellow Vouvray saved for just such an occasion."

170

"You have no suite, Leftwich," corrected Pulsifer in level tones. "On my way here, I bought the hotel and appointed Rightwich as manager in your stead. Let us hope that this has proved a salutary lesson to all."

"It has indeed," said the new manager, escorting us to the door as Leftwich was led away to become a dishwasher. "The next time you visit this fleabag, you will be greeted by a lobbyful of *schlemiehls* and nincompoops that will curl your hair." And with a genial wave, he placed his foot in the small of our backs and gave us a comradely shove into the stream of humanity eddying past the San Culotte.

SLEEPY-TIME
EXTRA

WHEN it was first noised along Publishers' Row that the John B. Pierce Foundation, a non-profit research organization, had instituted a survey dealing with American family behavior, attitudes, and possessions, public opinion was instantly split into two camps—into the larger, and drowsier, of which I fell. There is nothing like a good, painstaking survey full of decimal points and guarded generalizations to put a glaze like a Sung vase on your eyeball. Even the fact that the results of the poll were to be printed in that most exciting of current periodicals, *Business Week,* did little to allay my fatigue. Then, one morning in early April, hell started popping at my corner

stationery store. "What's good today, Clinton?"
I asked, browsing over the magazine rack. "Well,
I tell you," replied Clinton, thoughtfully scratching the stubble on his chin (he raised corn there
last year but is letting it lie fallow this season),
"we just got the new number of *Business Week*
containing the John B. Pierce Foundation survey
on American family behavior, attitudes, and possessions." "Well, dog my cats!" I exclaimed,
struck all of a heap. "Let's have a nickel's worth
of those licorice gumdrops, will you, Clinton?"
"Sure," said Clinton reluctantly, "but how about
this new number of *Business Week* containing the
John B. Pierce Foundation—" "Listen, Clinton,"
I said suddenly, "did you hear a funny little click
just then?" "Aha," breathed Clinton, round-eyed.
"What was it?" "A customer closing his account,"
I snapped, closing my account and taking my cus-
tom elsewhere.

It took a stray copy of the Buffalo *Evening
News*, abandoned late yesterday afternoon on my
bus seat by some upstate transient, to reveal the
true nature of the survey and dispel my apathy.
"Married Couples Favor Double Beds," trum-

peted the dispatch. "Eighty-seven per cent of husbands and wives sleep together in double beds but 5% of the wives are dissatisfied with this and 40% think maybe twin beds would be ideal, *Business Week* Magazine reported today on the basis of a survey by the John B. Pierce Foundation, nonprofit research organization. Other conclusions of the survey . . . included: In summer, 70.3% of the wives sleep in nightgowns, 24% in pajamas, 5% in the nude, and seven-tenths of 1% in shorts. Sixteen per cent of the women reported they would like to sleep in the nude, causing the Pierce Foundation to comment: 'Here we have clear-cut evidence of an inhibition.' . . . Fifty per cent of the husbands report no activity after getting into bed, 22% read, 12% talk, 7% listen to the radio, 3% say their prayers, 4% smoke, 2% eat. Comparable percentages for wives were 40% no activity, 29% read, 11% talk, 8% listen to the radio, 5% say their prayers, 3% think, 2% smoke, 2% eat."

Though one could speculate on the foregoing until the cows came home and distill all manner of savory psychological inferences, I cannot help wondering what machinery the Foundation used to obtain its statistics. Even the most incurious student of the report, I think, must ask himself eventually whether these delicious confidences were stammered into a telephone mouthpiece, or haltingly penned in a questionnaire, or whispered to a clear-eyed, bedirndled Bennington girl at the kitchen door. Somehow there is a grim, authoritative quality about the project which convinces me that the researchers went right to the source for their data, and I venture to think that more than one must have found himself embroiled in a situation like the following:

[Scene: The bedroom of the Stringfellows, a standard middle-aged couple. Monty Stringfellow is a large, noisy extrovert who conceals his insecurity under a boisterous good humor. He affects heavy, hobnailed Scotch brogues and leather patches at the elbows of his sports jackets, is constantly roaring out songs commanding you to quaff the nut-brown ale, and interlards his speech with salty imprecations like "Gadzooks" and "By my halidom." Tanagra, his wife, is a sultry, dis-

*contented creature on whom fifteen years of life
with a jolly good fellow have left their mark. As
the curtain rises, Monty, in a tweed nightgown, is
seated upright in their double bed singing a rol-
licking tune, to which he beats time with a pewter
tankard and a churchwarden pipe. Tanagra, a
sleep mask over her eyes, is trying to catch a little
shut-eye and getting nowhere.*]

MONTY (*con brio*):
   "Come quaff the nut-brown ale, lads,
   For youth is all too fleeting,
   We're holding high wassail, lads,
   And life's dull care unheeding,
   So quaff the nut-brown ale, lads—"

TANAGRA: Oh, shut up, for God's sake! You
and your nut-brown ale.

MONTY: What's wrong?

TANAGRA: Nothing. Nothing at all. What
makes you think anything's wrong?

MONTY: I don't know—you seem to be on edge
lately. Every time I open my mouth, you snap my
head off.

TANAGRA: Every time you open your mouth,

177

that blasted tune comes out. Haven't you anything else in your song bag?

MONTY: Gee, Tanagra, I always looked on it as our theme song, you might say. (*Sentimentally*) Don't you remember that first night at the Union Oyster House in Boston, when you made me sing it over and over?

TANAGRA: You swept me off my feet. I was just a silly little junior at Radcliffe.

MONTY: You—you mean our moment of enchantment has passed?

TANAGRA: I'll go further. Many's the night I've lain here awake studying your fat neck and praying for a bow string to tighten around it.

MONTY (*resentfully*): That's a heck of a thing to say. You keep up that kind of talk and pretty soon we'll be sleeping in twin beds.

TANAGRA: O. K. by me, chum.

VOICE (*under bed*): Aha!

MONTY: What's that? Who said that?

TANAGRA: I'm sure I don't know.

MONTY: There's somebody under this bed!

VOICE: There's nobody here except just us researchers from the John B. Pierce Foundation.

178

MONTY: W-what are you doing down there?

VOICE: Conducting a survey. (*Otis "Speedball" Ismay, ace statistician of the Foundation, a personable young executive, crawls into view from under the Stringfellow four-poster, flips open his notebook.*) Evening, friends. Close, isn't it?

TANAGRA (*archly*): I never realized how close.

ISMAY: You the lady of the house? I'd like to ask a few questions.

MONTY: Now just a minute. I don't know whether I approve—

TANAGRA: Batten down, stupid, he's not talking to you. (*Brightly*) Yes?

ISMAY: Let me see. You prefer sleeping in a nightgown rather than pajamas?

TANAGRA: Well, that depends. With this clod, a girl might as well wear a burlap bag.

ISMAY (*with a disparaging glance*): Yeah, strictly from Dixie. You know, that's a darned attractive nightie you've got on right now.

TANAGRA: What, *this* old thing?

ISMAY: It sends *me*, and I'm a tough customer. What do they call these doodads along the top?

TANAGRA: Alençon lace.

179

ISMAY: Cunning, aren't they?

TANAGRA (*provocatively*): Think so?

ISMAY (*tickling her*): Ootsie-kootsie!

TANAGRA: Now you stop, you bad boy.

MONTY: Hey, this is a pretty peculiar survey, if you ask me.

TANAGRA: Nobody asked you.

ISMAY: Wait a second. You *could* tell me one thing, Mister—Mister—

MONTY: Stringfellow. Monty Stringfellow.

ISMAY: Do you belong to any lodges, fraternal associations, or secret societies?

MONTY: What kind do you mean?

ISMAY (*impatiently*): It doesn't matter. Any kind that keeps you busy evenings.

MONTY: Why, yes. I'm Past Grand Chalice of the Golden Cupbearers of the World, field secretary of the Rice Institute Alumni—

ISMAY: Fine, fine. Don't bother to list them. We merely wish to know what evenings you spend away from home.

MONTY: Every Tuesday and every other Friday. Is this all part of the survey?

ISMAY: Part? It's practically the lifeblood. Well,

I think you've given me all the information I need. Oh, just one more detail, Mrs. Stringfellow. You understand there's a high percentage of error in an informal cross-section of this type and naturally we like to check our findings.

TANAGRA: Naturally.

ISMAY: I'd ask you to drop in at my office, but it's being redecorated.

TANAGRA: Yes, I read something in the paper to that effect. Is it serious?

ISMAY: No, no, it'll be all right in a day or two. For the time being, I've moved my charts and figures to the Weylin Bar, third table on the left as you come in at four-fifteen tomorrow afternoon.

TANAGRA: I'll be there half an hour early.

ISMAY: Splendid. (*To Stringfellow*) Thanks, old man, don't bother to show me to the door; I'll use the fire escape. Couple more calls to make in the building. Good night, all! (*He goes.*)

MONTY (*chortling*): Ho ho, that bird certainly pulled the wool over your eyes! He's no statistician. He didn't even have a fountain pen!

TANAGRA (*placidly*): Well, I swan. He sure took me in.

181

MONTY: Yes siree bob, you've got to get up pretty early in the morning to fool old Monty Stringfellow! (*He slaps her thigh familiarly and Tanagra sets her alarm for six forty-five.*)

CURTAIN

DENTAL OR MENTAL,
I SAY IT'S SPINACH

A FEW days ago, under the heading, MAN LEAPS OUT WINDOW AS DENTIST GETS FORCEPS, The New York Times reported the unusual case of a man who leaped out a window as the dentist got the forceps. Briefly, the circumstances were these. A citizen in Staten Island tottered into a dental parlor and, indicating an aching molar, moaned, "It's killing me. You've got to pull it out." The dentist grinned like a Cheshire cat— The New York Times neglected to say so, but a Cheshire cat who was present at the time grinned like a dentist—and reached for his instruments. "There was a leap and a crash," continues the account. "The astonished dentist saw his patient

183

spring through the closed window and drop ten feet to the sidewalk, where he lay dazed." The casualty was subsequently treated at a near-by hospital for abrasion and shock by Drs. J. G. Abrazian and Walter Shock, and then, like a worm, crept back to the dentist, apologized and offered to pay for the damage. On one point, however, he remained curiously adamant. He still has his tooth.

As a party who recently spent a whole morning with his knees braced against a dentist's chest, whimpering "Don't—don't—I'll do anything, but don't drill!" I am probably the only man in America equipped to sympathize with the poor devil. Ever since Nature presented me at birth with a set of thirty-two flawless little pearls of assorted sizes, I never once relaxed my vigilant stewardship of same. From the age of six onward, I constantly polished the enamel with peanut brittle, massaged the incisors twice daily with lollipops, and chewed taffy and chocolate-covered caramels faithfully to exercise the gums. As for consulting a dentist regularly, my punctuality practically amounted to a fetish. Every twelve

184

years I would drop whatever I was doing and allow wild Caucasian ponies to drag me to a reputable orthodontist. I guess you might say I was hipped on the subject of dental care.

When, therefore, I inadvertently stubbed a tooth on a submerged cherry in an old-fashioned last week and my toupee ricocheted off the ceiling, I felt both dismayed and betrayed. By eleven the next morning, I was seated in the antechamber of one Russell Pipgrass, D.D.S., limply holding a copy of the National Geographic upside down and pretending to be absorbed in Magyar folkways. Through the door communicating with the arena throbbed a thin, blood-curdling whine like a circular saw biting into a green plank. Suddenly an ear-splitting shriek rose above it, receding into a choked gurgle. I nonchalantly tapped out my cigarette in my eardrum and leaned over to the nurse, a Medusa type with serpents writhing out from under her prim white coif.

"Ah—er—pardon me," I observed, swallowing a bit of emery paper I had been chewing. "Did you hear anything just then?"

185

"Why, no," she replied, primly tucking back a snake under her cap. "What do you mean?"

"A—kind of a scratchy sound," I faltered.

"Oh, that," she sniffed carelessly. "Impacted wisdom tooth. We have to go in through the skull for those, you know." Murmuring some inconsequential excuse about lunching with a man in Sandusky, Ohio, I dropped to the floor and was creeping toward the corridor on all fours when Doctor Pipgrass emerged, rubbing his hands. "Well, here's an unexpected windfall!" he cackled, his eyes gleaming with cupidity. "Look out— slam the door on him!" Before I could dodge past, he pinioned me in a hammer lock and bore me, kicking and struggling, into his web. He was trying to wrestle me into the chair when the nurse raced in, brandishing a heavy glass ash tray.

"Here, hit him with this!" she panted.

"No, no, we mustn't bruise him," muttered Pipgrass. "Their relatives always ask a lot of silly questions." They finally made me comfy by strapping me into the chair with half a dozen towels, tilted my feet up and pried open my teeth with a

186

spoon. "Now then, where are his X-rays?" demanded the doctor.

"We haven't any," returned the nurse. "This is the first time he's been here."

"Well, bring me any X-rays," her employer barked. "What difference does it make? When you've seen one tooth, you've seen them all." He held up the X-rays against the light and examined them critically. "Well, friend, you're in a peck of trouble," he said at length. "You may as well know the worst. These are the teeth of an eighty-year-old man. You got here just in time." Plucking a horrendous nozzle from the rack, he shot compressed air down my gullet that sent me into a strangled paroxysm, and peered curiously at my inlays.

"Who put those in, a steamfitter?" he sneered. "You ought to be arrested for walking around with a job like that." He turned abruptly at the rustle of greenbacks and glared at his nurse. "See here, Miss Smedley, how many times have I told you not to count the patient's money in front of him? Take the wallet outside and go through it there." She nodded shamefacedly and slunk out.

187

"That's the kind of thing that creates a bad impression on the layman," growled Doctor Pipgrass, poking at my tongue with a sharp stick. "Now what seems to be the trouble in there?"

"Ong ong ong," I wheezed.

"H'm'm'm, a cleft palate," he mused. "Just as I feared. And you've got between four and five thousand cavities. While we're at it, I think we'd better tear out those lowers with a jackhammer and put in some nice expensive crowns. Excuse me." He quickly dialed a telephone number. "Is that you, Irene?" he asked. "Russell. Listen, on that white mink coat we were talking about at breakfast—go right ahead, I've changed my mind. . . . No, I'll tell you later. He's filthy with it."

"Look, doctor," I said with a casual yawn. "It's nothing really—just a funny tickling sensation in that rear tooth. I'll be back Tuesday—a year from Tuesday."

"Yes, yes," he interrupted, patting me reassuringly. "Don't be afraid now; this won't hurt a bit." With a slow, cunning smile, he produced from behind his back a hypodermic of the type used on brewery horses and, distending my lip,

188

plunged it into the gum. The tip of my nose instantly froze, and my tongue took on the proportions of a bolt of flannel. I tried to cry out, but my larynx was out to lunch. Seizing the opportunity, Pipgrass snatched up his drill, took a firm purchase on my hair and teed off. A mixture of sensation, roughly comparable to being alternately stilettoed and inflated with a bicycle pump, overcame me; two thin wisps of smoke curled upward slowly from my ears. Fortunately, I had been schooled from boyhood to withstand pain without flinching, and beyond an occasional scream that rattled the windows, I bore myself with the stoicism of a red man. Scarcely ninety minutes later, Doctor Pipgrass thrust aside the drill, wiped his streaming forehead and shook the mass of protoplasm before him.

"Well, we're in the home stretch," he announced brightly, extracting a rubber sheet from a drawer. "We'll put this dam on you and fill her in a jiffy. You don't get claustrophobia, do you?"

"Wh-what's that?" I squeaked.

"Fear of being buried alive," he explained

189

smoothly. "Kind of a stifling feeling. Your heart starts racing and you think you're going crazy. Pure imagination, of course." He pinned the rubber sheet over my face, slipped it over the tooth and left me alone with my thoughts. In less time than it takes to relate, I was a graduate member, *summa cum laude*, of the Claustrophobia Club. My face had turned a stunning shade of green, my heart was going like Big Ben, and a set of castanets in my knees was playing the Malagueña. Summoning my last reserves of strength, I cast off my bonds and catapulted through the anteroom to freedom. I bequeathed Pipgrass a fleece-lined overcoat worth sixty-eight dollars, and he's welcome to it; I'll string along nicely with this big wad of chewing gum over my tooth. On me it looks good.

AMO, AMAS, AMAT,
AMAMUS, AMATIS, ENOUGH

YESTERDAY morning I awoke in a pool of glori-
ous golden sunshine laced with cracker crumbs
to discover that spring had returned to Washington Square. A pair of pigeons were cooing gently
directly beneath my window; two squirrels
plighted their troth in a branch overhead; at the
corner a handsome member of New York's finest
twirled his nightstick and cast roguish glances at
the saucy-eyed flower vendor. The scene could
have been staged only by a Lubitsch; in fact,
Lubitsch himself was seated on a bench across the
street, smoking a cucumber and looking as cool
as a cigar. It lacked only Nelson Eddy to appear
on a penthouse terrace and loose a chorus of deep-

191

throated song, and, as if by magic, Nelson Eddy suddenly appeared on a penthouse terrace and, with the artistry that has made his name a word, launched into an aria. A moment later, Jeanette MacDonald, in creamy negligee, joined the dashing rascal, making sixty-four teeth, and the lovers began a lilting duet. The passers-by immediately took up the refrain; windows flew up at the Brevoort, flew down again; the melody spread rapidly up Fifth Avenue, debouched into Broadway, detoured into Park, and soon the entire city was humming the infectious strain in joyous tribute to Jeanette's and Nelson's happiness.

Caught up in the mood of the moment, I donned a jaunty foulard bow, stuck a feather in my hatband and one in my throat, and set out to look over spring fashions in love. That I ultimately wound up with a slight puff under one eye and a warning from a policewoman is not germane to the discussion. Truth is a wood violet that blooms in the least likely corner, and I found it in a couple of obscure pulp magazines called *Gay Love Stories* and *Ideal Love*, which retail at a dime apiece. Twenty cents for a postgraduate

192

course in passion— *entre nous,* kids, I think I've got the only game in town.

Biologically, it was reassuring to find that the war had wrought no intrinsic change in the characters who people cut-rate romantic fiction; the smooth and deadly function of the glands continues undisturbed by the roar of high explosives. The ladies are as cuddly and adorable as they were before Pearl Harbor, the cavaliers as manly and chivalrous as any immortalized by Nell Brinkley and Leyendecker. Consider, for instance, Linda Marshall, the colleen of "Little Ball of Catnip," in the May *Ideal Love,* as she stands lost in dreams in her garden at Santa Monica, "slender and poised in a brown and white seersucker dress, the tight bodice cunningly trimmed in rickrack braid. She had a clear skin, nicely accented by dark eyebrows, lively hazel eyes, and beautifully fashioned cherry-red lips. The general impression was that of youth on the wing." Incidentally, there seems to be a strange, almost Freudian compulsion in both magazines to describe the heroine in avian terms—*vide* Kitty Malcolm in "Barefoot Blonde" (*Gay Love*): "That evening, after finish-

193

ing a careful toilette, Kitty glanced at herself in the mirror, and knew that she had never looked lovelier. The black velvet gown molded her slim figure to perfection. In the gleaming nest of curls which she had scooped atop her head, Steve's gardenias, which had arrived via messenger, provided the last, elegant touch." It seems almost picayune of Steve not to have included a clutch of cold-storage eggs, or at least a nice fat worm, for the nest atop his inamorata's head as an earnest of eventual domesticity.

An even more tempting *bonne bouche* than Kitty is Bonita Kellsinger, grooming her lovely frame for the evening in "Shadow of Her Past" (*Gay Love*, June): "The very thought of such a triumph [winning the richest boy in Barnesville] brought roses to her richly tanned cheeks, brought a fiery sparkle into her wide, greenish-blue eyes. She brushed her thick, ripe-wheat colored hair until it hung on her straight slender shoulders in rich gleaming waves. A pair of small jewelled clips held back one wave of hair on either side of the girl's high, intelligent forehead. She made an enticing red rosebud of her mouth, and wound

194

ropes of scarlet wooden beads around her neck and arms." Small wonder indeed that her gallant fidgets impatiently off scene at the wheel of his station wagon, which the author introduces parenthetically in one of the most syncopated bits of whitewash on record: "Cary had explained that he couldn't get adequate rations of gas for any of his cars but the wagon, which he used in working hours to haul people to and from his canning factory that was so busy putting up dehydrated foods for the Army and Navy." For sheer pith, the passage deserves a niche in the Hall of Exposition beside my all-time favorite, which graced one of the early Fu Manchu films. Briefly, the artful Doctor had eluded Nayland Smith by swarming down a rope ladder into the Thames. The ensuing scene revealed a vast underground cavern, in the foreground a rough deal table piled high with crucibles, alembics, and retorts bubbling with sinister compounds. After a pause, the table swung away, a trapdoor opened, and Dr. Fu crept up, followed by a henchman (Tully Marshall). "Well, Wing Chang," remarked the Doctor with a fiendish chuckle, "these old dye works certainly

195

make an admirable laboratory of crime, do they not?"

Since every one of the nineteen novelettes and short stories I dipped into was written by a woman, the result is a gallery of fairly glamorous males, nearly all of them named Michael. It is practically six, two, and even that at some point in the action tiny muscles are going to flicker in lean jaws, eyes crinkle up quizzically at the corners, and six feet of lanky, bronzed strength strain a reluctant miss against a rough khaki shoulder (apparently the supply of smooth khaki shoulders has been exhausted, for whatever reason). There must have been a singularly dreamy look in the eye of Betty Webb Lucas, the author of "Blue Angel," (*Gay Love*), when she hatched Dr. Michael Halliday, chief surgeon of the City Hospital: "He was more like a Greek god, in spite of the flaming hair that threatened to break into rebellious curls at any moment, and the sterile white jacket straining over broad shoulders. His eyes were incredibly blue, and his sun-bronzed skin made them seem bluer still." Much as I respect honest emotion, I am afraid Miss Lucas became a trifle too dreamy in her medical dialogue: "Judy could only stare until he said impatiently: 'Haven't you anything else to do but stand there peering at me like a—a biological specie?'" The most charitable assumption in defense of Miss Lucas must be that the dear nearness of Judy in her crisp white nurse's uniform unnerved the eminent man.

It is hardly surprising that when these golden lads and lasses finally have at one another, they produce an effect akin to the interior of a blast furnace. Observe the Wagnerian encounter between the aforementioned Bonita Kellsinger and her beau ideal: "He caught her close to him, pinned her cheek against the rough khaki shoulder of his uniform, and slowly, deliberately covered her mouth with his, in a kiss that made her forget everything for the moment in the heady rapture of it. . . . They seemed to ascend to the top of a very high mountain, where there hung a white disc of moon in a sparkling bed of stars, and a soft breeze scented with jasmine swept over them. But when his lips lifted from hers, it was as though the cables had been cut from an elevator.

197

She hit earth with a bump that shocked her awake." While Bonita brushes the meteorites from her hair and recovers her land legs, take a hinge at Lieutenant Lex McClure flinging a bit of woo in "Glass Walls are Cold" (*Ideal*): "Sally fought against it, but she felt as though she would die of the ecstasy that poured through her body. All of her senses quickened and became alert. She smelled the piney fragrance of his tobacco [that mixture of sun-dried burley and evergreen cones so popular of late with the armed forces] and the light scent of her own perfume. Her lips softened under his pressure, then she drew away softly, drawing her cheek across his chin, feeling the roughness of his day-old beard." Luckily, as one weaned on *The Perfumed Garden* and the Mardrus translation of *The Arabian Nights*, I was able to withstand this erotic byplay. Even so, I must confess that a bestial flush invaded my cheek and I had to fight off an overmastering impulse to pinch the hired girl.

At the risk of slighting any individual author, I must say the brightest star in the galaxy is unquestionably Leonora McPheeters whose "Perfumed

198

Slacker" (*Ideal*, May) is subheaded "How could you love a man who always smelled like a boudoir?" For timeliness, melodrama, and a good old-fashioned concupiscence like Mother used to make, I haven't met its equal since the *Decameron*. The principals in this droll tale are two: John Craig, "tall, masculine, tweedy . . . a big overgrown Newfoundland pup, with his rough tawny hair and steady brown eyes," and Judy, a *zäftick* little proposition bent on bringing him to heel. Ostensibly the pair are engaged in running a cosmetic laboratory; actually, they seem to spend the business day mousing around each other, trading molten kisses and generally overheating themselves. Occasionally Judy varies the routine by kissing Bob, a shadowy member in a soldier suit who drifts in from an unspecified reservation, but these ersatz embraces only sharpen her appetite for the brand of judo dispensed by Craig. Unfortunately, the intra-office romance withers when Judy detects her employer's lack of enthusiasm for military service, and excoriating him for a coward and a caitiff, she gives him the mitten. Then, in a whirlwind denouement, she captures two enemy

199

agents by upsetting a carboy of wave set over their heads and learns to her stupefaction that Craig has really been evolving explosives for the government. As the curtain descends, Philemon seizes Baucis in a sizzling hammer lock, superbly indifferent to the fact that they are standing ankle-deep in thermite and TNT, and rains kisses on her upturned face.

By one of those coincidences that are positively spooky, the hired girl opened my door at this juncture and found the boss-man ankle-deep in a roomful of shredded pulp fiction, baying like a timber wolf. Before she could turn to flee, five feet seven of lanky, bronzed strength reached out and strained her against a rough pajama shoulder. I'm still trying to explain things to the employment agency, but they keep hanging up on me. You don't know anybody with full-fashioned cherry-red lips and a high, intelligent forehead who could help me with the housework, do you? She needn't bother about a uniform; just tell her to meet me in the Lombardy Bar at five tomorrow. They've got the best Dutch Cleanser in town.

PULL DEVIL,
PULL BEAGLE

A GOOD many years ago, about the time that "Perdicaris Alive or Raisuli Dead" was on everyone's tongue and I could quote Louise Glaum's bust measurement to the fraction of an inch, I conceived an idea for a play. Briefly, it was to deal with a group of people in a shabby boarding house, into whose midst would come a mysterious stranger with infinite compassion and a face illumined from within by a light not of this world. By the time the final curtain fell, this character (whom I clearly saw being played by H. B. Warner) would reconcile the lovers, rehabilitate a wanton, vindicate a suspected embezzler, restore crotchety old Miss Sprague's faith in hu-

201

manity, and vanish without betraying his identity. Word of my project must have leaked out, because I had hardly procured several stout nibs and a packet of foolscap from the corner stationery stoor when *The Passing of the Third Floor Back* appeared and overnight I became a pariah.

It was a bitter draught, but I swallowed it. For a long time I lay fallow, and then another idea—this time for a novel—slowly took form in my mind. It would mirror the disillusion and moral bankruptcy of postwar English society, a subject with which I was intimately acquainted. I chose as heroine a woman of singular beauty, beauty that bade fair to destroy the men it attracted. I planned to make Orchid Marsh the symbol of decadent Mayfair—brittle, reckless, yet somehow as gallant and splendid as the hat she wore. The suicide of her husband as a gesture of purity, her feverish succession of affairs with cads and wastrels, her tragic self-destruction at the wheel of a high-powered roadster—innumerable details suggested themselves as I legged it to the stationery store. The clerk was just wrapping up my nibs and foolscap when I idly picked up a new novel called *The Green Hat.* . . .Well, I am the last to begrudge Michael Arlen his success. He merely got the story down on paper before I did. All the same, it's pretty rough when it happens twice in a lifetime. And when it happens a *third* time, you begin to get a thoughtful little line between the eyebrows.

The third time, specifically, was one night a few weeks ago, when I picked up Sidney Skolsky's movie column and read the following: "Julie Haydon has sold a book containing just love letters to her dog. It will be published by Marcel Rodd." Now, it goes without saying that the love letters of a celebrated actress to her dog are a juicy plum in any publishing season and Mr. Rodd may be pardoned for smacking his lips. Ironically enough, however, one week before, I had concluded arrangements with Mr. Spencer Gouge of Fly-By-Night Editions to issue a volume of love letters written to me by a young beagle I bought this summer. The felicity of phrase, the emotional maturity which mark these letters would be arresting in a full-grown dog; in a six-months-old puppy, they are nothing short of extraordinary.

203

Nevertheless, since a book by a famous personality like Miss Haydon must overshadow one by an obscure beagle, and since I have no desire to queer her pitch, I have decided to withdraw the dog's letters from publication. I submit only a few to convince possible skeptics of their authenticity and flavor. If they occasionally verge on the fulsome, it should be remembered that the dog was very much in love with me at the moment. I subsequently had occasion to kick him downstairs several times and his affection may have cooled somewhat.

SEPTEMBER 9

DEAR CHIEF,

What a privilege it is to live in the same house with someone like you. Whenever I hear people talking behind your back, saying things like "He's nursing the first nickel he ever made" and "Can you imagine seeing that phiz over a breakfast table?," it makes my blood boil. All right, so you *are* a bit stingy with your money. So you *do* trip over your feet when you walk. So your head *does* come to a point on top. Whose fault is that? You can't help those things any more than I can

204

help having eleven champions in my pedigree and a blood line that goes back six hundred years.

Incidentally, since we're on the subject of ancestry, I happened to run across your family album while chewing up some of your books. Those relatives of yours certainly are a weird lot—all shapes and sizes. Some real killers there, boy. Of course this heredity business is bunk and all that, but don't you think people would be a lot less critical of you if they could have a look at your genealogy? I mean to say, you don't expect to find a prize pippin in a barrel of rotten apples. Now, take my folks, on the other hand. My great-grandfather was best of breed three years running at Westminster—silver cups all over the place. He sired Saddlerock Nainsook Bravo, who belonged to the former lieutenant governor of West Virginia. With that kind of stock, you get real character. See the difference, old man?

Up to now, I've hesitated to broach the food situation to you, but you might as well know what's going on in your own household. Yesterday your wife chipped the rust off her change purse and bought me a pat of hamburger, just

205

large enough to engrave the Lord's Prayer on. The minute she left the kitchen, the maid swallowed it. I gave her a good bite in the flank, but it didn't taste the same. I'm telling you, boss, I've had all the ersatz I intend to eat. If I don't get some protein pretty soon, you'd better watch those children of yours.

In fact, you'd better watch a lot of things, among them the people in the flat next door to you. Did you know that the lady who lives there came home the other evening and found her husband washing a couple of ghosts in the bathtub? There was a very penetrating smell of Coty perfume in the air, and she asked what he was doing. "Why, nothing, dear," he replied. "I'm just separating the chypre from the ghosts." Now, what do you make of that?

Yours devotedly,
FLASH

SEPTEMBER 27

DEAR CHIEF,

I'm no doctor, but I'll give you some friendly advice. That shade of purple you've taken to turning recently, every time anything unusual happens, has me worried. One minute you're your usual shark's-belly white, and the next, without any transition, you look like an eggplant. Better watch the old temper, Mac.

For instance, Tuesday night when you came home from the movies. O.K., somebody had short-circuited the lamps, eaten a hole in the sofa, and strewn kapok all over the floor. It might have been anyone—that part-time peon of yours or those part-time chimpanzees masquerading as children. Had you asked me, I could have told you that your domestic lost three previous jobs because of her appetite for sofas. Instead, you chased me through the apartment, screaming the most bloodcurdling oaths and flailing around with a broom. Personally, I enjoyed the romp and slept beautifully afterward, even if you did puff like a donkey engine all night long. Don't play bean-bag with your arteries, brother, or you'll wind up in a rolling chair at French Lick.

Speaking of health, maybe you'd like to know what kind of starvation diet one member of the family unit is subsisting on. For dinner today, I

207

was fed a moist mash containing these certified
ingredients: soybean flour, wheat middlings, dried
whey, yeast culture, manganese sulphate, oyster-
shell flour, bone meal, and limestone. Some beano,
eh? Nothing like limestone to stick to the ribs. To
top it off, I come into the dining room and find
you, with your napkin tucked in below your third
chin, gorging yourself on pot roast, baked potato,
buttered carrots, chocolate cake, and coffee. All it
needed to complete the composition was a big
platter and an apple in your mouth.

I can't figure out the Imbries, those neighbors
on our floor. I overheard Mrs. Imbrie telling the
elevator boy that they've got a drunken Balkan
couple at their country place who are constantly
smashing up this little army truck they use. One
night last week-end, Imbrie heard a crash near
the bar and ran out to investigate. After a while,
his wife called from a bedroom window and asked
what he was doing. "Why, nothing, dear," Imbrie called back. "I'm just separating the jeep
from the Croats." Maybe you can make head or
tail of it; it's beyond me.

Adoringly,
FLASH

208

DEAR CHIEF,

Every time I've come into the room the past few days, there's been more intrigue and buzzing than backstage at the Russian ballet. Do you think I don't realize what those sickly smiles and sudden endearments signify? You've got it all fixed to get me out of the way; I know too much. Well, if that's the way you want to play it, go ahead. But before you hire a couple of mongrels to waylay me up a dark alley, or ship me off to the kennel, or whatever you're cooking up, you may as well know the score.

As you read this, the O.P.A. and the S.P.C.A. each has in its respective safe a sealed envelope, to be opened within forty-eight hours after I disappear. The first contains a highly illuminating graph analyzing the recurrence of pot roast, steak, and other rationed meats on your menu. The second is a documented account of such starvation and maltreatment of a small animal as has rarely been compiled in our time. Both of these communications could be so extremely embarrassing that I'm sure you'd prefer to sit down with me and work out a modus vivendi. . . . I always say "blackmail" is such an ugly word, don't you? Call it, rather, a gentleman's agreement.

For after all, that is what we both are—gentlemen. The mere fact that my kin have run with the Quorn pack for sixteen generations and yours still wear ready-made clothing is irrelevant; I refuse to judge a man by his atrocious table manners or his gaudy hand-me-downs. He may be a wife-beater, turncoat, sycophant, and moral beachcomber, but underneath, deep down, one can discern fugitive traces of decency. Perhaps, if there were enough top round in it for me, I could show him the road to salvation.

As for that Imbrie couple in the next apartment, I've frankly given up trying to comprehend their behavior. Last night they threw a big cocktail party jammed with Broadway celebrities, columnists, and what all. Halfway through it, a violent altercation started between a radical journalist and some lady war correspondent named Alice Leone something or other—I didn't catch the last part. Imbrie finally had to step in and break it up, and his wife asked him what he was doing. "Why, nothing, dear," he assured her. "I'm just separating the creep from the Moats." Of course, I heard this through the wall and I may have missed a word or two.

Well, *hasta luego*, kiddo, and keep your nose clean. If I don't hear from you before, I'll see you in the Tombs.

Eternally yours,
FLASH

HOW SHARPER THAN
A SERPENT'S TOOTH

THE other evening, with nobody levelling a gun at my temple, I deserted a well-sprung arm-chair and a gripping novel, sloshed forty blocks uptown in a freezing rain, and, together with five hundred other bats, hung from the rafters at Loew's Strabismus to see Joan Crawford's latest vehicle, *Mildred Pierce*. Certain critics, assessing the film, maintained that Miss Crawford rose to heights never before scaled. Whether she did or not, I certainly did; the only person higher than me was the projectionist, who kept flicking ashes down my coat collar and sneezing so convulsively that twice during the performance my head rolled down the balcony steps. Oh, I was kept busy, I can tell you, running downstairs to retrieve it and following the story at the same time. Yet even under these trying conditions, aggravated by the circumstance that someone had liberated a powerful sleep-inducing drug among the audience, I was gripped by a brief passage between the star and her daughter, played by Ann Blyth. It had been established that Joan, eager to give the child every advantage, had worked tirelessly as a waitress, shielding the fact from her, and had eventually built up a chain of restaurants. Ann, though, inevitably discovers her mother's plebeian calling, and at the proper kinetic moment her disdain boils over in a speech approximately as follows: "Faugh, you disgust me. You reek of the kitchen, of blue plates and sizzling platters. You bring with you the smell of grease and short-order frying, you—you restaurateur, you!" At that juncture, unluckily, the projectionist sneezed again, with such force that I was blown clear into the lobby and out into Times Square, and deciding that it would be tempting fate to return to my perch, I sloshed quickly downtown while the sloshing was good.

Reviewing the scene in my mind (or, more

214

properly, what remained of the scene in what remained of my mind), I realized that however fruity the phrasing, its psychology was eminently sound. The instinct to conceal one's true livelihood from the kiddies, for fear of their possible scorn, is as normal as snoring. A highly solvent gentleman in Forest Hills, a vestryman and the father of three, once told me in wine that for thirty years, under twelve different pseudonyms, he had supplied the gamiest kind of pulp fiction to *Snappy Stories* and *Flynn's*, although his children believed him to be a stockbroker. The plumper the poke, the more painful is any reference to its origin.

The most recent victim of indiscreet babble of this sort is Barbara Hutton Mdivani Reventlow Grant, with whose predicament Charles Ventura lately concerned himself in his society column in the *World-Telegram*. Wrote Mr. Ventura: "Relations between the chain-store heiress and her ex-husband, Kurt, are still strained. Barbara tells friends her most recent annoyance from Kurt came with the discovery he had gone out of his way to tell Lance his mother's money came from the ten-cent store."

The item poses all sorts of interesting questions.

215

What constitutes going out of your way to tell a lad his mother's money came from forty or fifty thousand ten-cent stores? How did Lance take the news? Did he, in the first shock of revelation, force his father to his knees and demand a retraction of the slur? Did he fling himself with a choked cry into the Countess's lap, all tears and disillusion, or did he heap coals on her head? Mr. Ventura does not say. Mr. Ventura, it would seem, is an old tease. With the implication that he has other fish to fry, he leaps straightway into the domestic problems of slim, attractive Yvette Helene LeRoux Townsend, leaving me in my ragged shawl out in the snow, holding Barbara Hutton's predicament. I hope that the dimly analogous situation which follows, served up for convenience in a dramatic fricassee, may shed some light on the matter and bring chaos out of confusion.

[Scene: *The library of the luxurious Park Avenue triplex of Mr. and Mrs. Milo Leotard Allardyce DuPlessis Weatherwax. The furnishings display taste but little ostentation: a couple of dozen Breughels, fifteen or twenty El Grecos, a sprinkling of Goyas, a smidgen of Vermeers. The room*

216

*has a lived-in air: a fistful of loose emeralds lies
undusted in an ashtray, and the few first folios in
evidence are palpably dog-eared. The curtain rises
on a note of marital discord. Octavia Weatherwax,
a chic, poised woman in her mid-forties, has just
picked up a bust of Amy Lowell by Epstein and
smashed it over her husband's head. Milo, a portly,
well-groomed man of fifty, spits out a tooth,
catches up a bust of Epstein by Amy Lowell, and
returns the compliment.*]

OCTAVIA (*brushing plaster from her coiffure*):
Listen, Milo, we can't go on this way.

MILO: Why not? I've still got this left. (*He
picks up a bust of Amy Epstein by Lowell
Thomas.*)

OCTAVIA: No, no, this is the handwriting on the
wall. Our marriage is washed up—napoo—*aus-
gespielt.*

MILO: Maybe you're right. I've felt for some
time that things haven't been the same between
us.

OCTAVIA: Oh, well, the fat's in the fire. How
are we to break the news to Rapier?

MILO: Rapier? What Rapier is that?

OCTAVIA: Why, our nineteen-year-old son,

217

which he's home from Yale on his midyears and don't suspicion that his folks are rifting.

Milo: Oh, yes. Where is our cub at the present writing?

Octavia: In the tack room, furbishing up the accoutrements of his polo ponies.

Milo (*acidly*): Far better off to be furbishing up on his Euclid, lest he drag the name of Weatherwax through the scholastic mire.

Octavia: Shhhh, here he comes now. (*The sound of expensive Scotch brogues approaching on a parquet floor is heard, an effect achieved by striking two coconut shells together.*) If you need me, I shall be laying down on my lounge with a vinegar compress. (*She exits as Rapier enters—a rather awkward bit of stagecraft, as they trip over each other, but if the play runs, the property man can always saw another door in the set. Rapier, albeit somewhat spoiled, is a blueblood to his fingertips, carries his head and feet as though to the manner born.*)

Rapier: Hiya, Jackson. What's buzzin', cousin?

Milo: Humph. Is that some more of your new-fangled college slang?

RAPIER: Don't be a sherbet, Herbert. (*Lighting a gold-monogrammed Egyptian Deity*) What's cookin', goodlookin'?

MILO (*gravely*): Son, I'm not going to mince words with you.

RAPIER: Don't mince, quince. I'm waitin', Satan.

MILO: My boy, the Weatherwax union has blown a gasket. Our frail matrimonial bark, buffeted by the winds of temperament, has foundered on the shoals of incompatibility.

RAPIER: Get in the groove, fatso. I don't latch onto that long-hair schmaltz.

MILO: To employ the vulgate, your mother and I have phhht.

RAPIER (*with quick sympathy*): That's rum, chum.

MILO: Yes, it's hard on us oldsters, but it isn't going to be easy for you, either.

RAPIER (*frightened*): You mean I've got to go to work?

MILO: Certainly *not*. As long as there's a penny of your mother's money left, we'll make out somehow.

219

RAPIER: Look guv'nor, I . . . that is, me . . . aw, cripes, can I ask you something man to man?

MILO (*aside*): I was afraid of this.

RAPIER: Well, I've been running with a pretty serious crowd up at New Haven—lots of bull sessions about swing and stuff—and I've been wondering. Where does our money come from?

MILO (*evasively*): Why—er—uh—the doctor brings it. In a little black bag.

RAPIER: Ah, gee, Dad, I'm old enough to know. *Please.*

MILO: There, there. Now run along and play with your ponies.

RAPIER: Wouldn't you rather tell me than have me learn it in the gutter?

MILO: We-e-ell, all right, but my, you children grow up quick nowadays. Have you ever heard of the Weatherwax All-Weather Garbage Disposal Plan?

RAPIER: You—you mean whereby garbage is disposed of in all weathers by having neatly uniformed attendants call for and remove it?

MILO: Yes. That is the genesis of our scratch.

RAPIER (*burying his face in his hands*): Oh, Daddy, I want to die!

MILO: Steady on, lad. After all, think of the millions which their flats would be a welter of chicken bones, fruit peels, and old tea bags were it not for our kindly ministrations.

RAPIER (*sobbing*): I'll never be able to hold up my head in Bulldog circles again.

MILO: Nonsense. Why, you wear the keenest threads on the campus and are persona grata to myriad Eli frats.

RAPIER (*his face drawn and a new maturity in his voice*): No, Father, this is the end of halcyon days in the groves of Academe. I'm going away.

MILO: Where?

RAPIER: Somewhere beyond the horizon—to fabled Cathay or Samarkand and Ind, if need be. Anywhere I can find other values than the tinkle of money and the clang of refuse cans.

MILO (*his eyes shining*): There speaks a Weatherwax, my boy. Here, I want you to have this little keepsake.

RAPIER: What is it?

MILO: A letter of credit for seven hundred grand. It won't buy much except dreams, but it belonged to your mother.

RAPIER: Thank you, sir. (*He starts out.*)

221

MILO: Wait a minute, I can't let you go like this. You'll need money, introductions, shelter—

RAPIER: I'll patch up that old private railroad car of mine—the one underneath the Waldorf-Astoria.

MILO: Take ours, too. It's only using up steam.

RAPIER (*simply*): I'm sorry, Dad. From now on I walk alone. Goodbye. (*He exits, colliding with his mother—there simply* must *be two doors in this set. Octavia looks back at him, puzzled.*)

OCTAVIA: Why, goodness, what ails the child? What's that exalted look on his face?

MILO: That, Octavia, is what a very great Russian named Louis Tolstoy once called "redemption."

OCTAVIA: Milo! You didn't tell—you couldn't—

MILO (*his shoulders bowed*): It just soaked in through his pores. (*Octavia, her eyes tragic, picks up a bronze caryatid, smashes it over his head, and exits. He shrugs, picks up a Greek bacchante loitering in the wings, and consoles himself.*)

CURTAIN

INSERT FLAP "A"
AND THROW AWAY

ONE stifling summer afternoon last August, in the attic of a tiny stone house in Pennsylvania, I made a most interesting discovery: the shortest, cheapest method of inducing a nervous breakdown ever perfected. In this technique (eventually adopted by the psychology department of Duke University, which will adopt anything), the subject is placed in a sharply sloping attic heated to 340°F. and given a mothproof closet known as the Jiffy-Cloz to assemble. The Jiffy-Cloz, procurable at any department store or neighborhood insane asylum, consists of half a dozen gigantic sheets of red cardboard, two plywood doors, a clothes rack, and a packet of staples. With these

223

is included a set of instructions mimeographed in pale-violet ink, fruity with phrases like "Pass Section F through Slot AA, taking care not to fold tabs behind washers (see Fig. 9)." The cardboard is so processed that as the subject struggles convulsively to force the staple through, it suddenly buckles, plunging the staple deep into his thumb. He thereupon springs up with a dolorous cry and smites his knob (Section K) on the rafters (RR). As a final demonic touch, the Jiffy-Cloz people cunningly omit four of the staples necessary to finish the job, so that after indescribable purgatory, the best the subject can possibly achieve is a sleazy, capricious structure which would reduce any self-respecting moth to helpless laughter. The cumulative frustration, the tropical heat, and the soft, ghostly chuckling of the moths are calculated to unseat the strongest mentality.

In a period of rapid technological change, however, it was inevitable that a method as cumbersome as the Jiffy-Cloz would be superseded. It was superseded at exactly nine-thirty Christmas morning by a device called the Self-Running 10-Inch Scale-Model Delivery-Truck Kit Powered by

Magic Motor, costing twenty-nine cents. About nine on that particular morning, I was spread-eagled on my bed, indulging in my favorite sport of mouth-breathing, when a cork fired from a child's air gun mysteriously lodged in my throat. The pellet proved awkward for a while, but I finally ejected it by flailing the little marksman (and his sister, for good measure) until their welkins rang, and sauntered in to breakfast. Before I could choke down a healing fruit juice, my consort, a tall, regal creature indistinguishable from Cornelia, the Mother of the Gracchi, except that her foot was entangled in a roller skate, swept in. She extended a large, unmistakable box covered with diagrams.

"Now don't start making excuses," she whined. "It's just a simple cardboard toy. The directions are on the back—"

"Look, dear," I interrupted, rising hurriedly and pulling on my overcoat, "it clean slipped my mind. I'm supposed to take a lesson in crosshatching at Zim's School of Cartooning today."

"On Christmas?" she asked suspiciously.

"Yes, it's the only time they could fit me in," I

225

countered glibly. "This is the big week for cross-hatching, you know, between Christmas and New Year's."

"Do you think you ought to go in your pajamas?" she asked.

"Oh, that's O.K.," I smiled. "We often work in our pajamas up at Zim's. Well, goodbye now. If I'm not home by Thursday, you'll find a cold snack in the safe-deposit box." My subterfuge, unluckily, went for naught, and in a trice I was sprawled on the nursery floor, surrounded by two lambkins and ninety-eight segments of the Self-Running 10-Inch Scale-Model Delivery-Truck Construction Kit.

The theory of the kit was simplicity itself, easily intelligible to Kettering of General Motors, Professor Millikan, or any first-rate physicist. Taking as my starting point the only sentence I could comprehend, "Fold down on all lines marked 'fold down;' fold up on all lines marked 'fold up,'" I set the children to work and myself folded up with an album of views of Chili Williams. In a few moments, my skin was suffused with a delightful tingling sensation and I was ready for the second phase, lightly referred to in the directions

226

as "Preparing the Spring Motor Unit." As nearly as I could determine after twenty minutes of mumbling, the Magic Motor ("No Electricity—No Batteries—Nothing to Wind—Motor Never Wears Out") was an accordion-pleated affair operating by torsion, attached to the axles. "It is necessary," said the text, "to cut a slight notch in each of the axles with a knife (see Fig. C.). To find the exact place to cut this notch, lay one of the axles over diagram at bottom of page."

"Well, *now* we're getting someplace!" I boomed, with a false gusto that deceived nobody. "Here, Buster, run in and get Daddy a knife."

"I dowanna," quavered the boy, backing away. "You always cut yourself at this stage." I gave the wee fellow an indulgent pat on the head that flattened it slightly, to teach him civility, and commandeered a long, serrated bread knife from the kitchen. "Now watch me closely, children," I ordered. "We place the axle on the diagram as in Fig. C, applying a strong downward pressure on the knife handle at all times." The axle must have been a factory second, because an instant later I was in the bathroom grinding my teeth in agony and attempting to stanch the flow of blood. Ultimately, I succeeded in contriving a rough bandage and slipped back into the nursery without awaking the children's suspicions. An agreeable surprise awaited me. Guided by a mechanical bent clearly inherited from their sire, the rascals had put together the chassis of the delivery truck.

"Very good indeed," I complimented (naturally, one has to exaggerate praise to develop a child's self-confidence). "Let's see—what's the next step? Ah, yes. 'Lock into box shape by inserting tabs C, D, E, F, G, H, J, K, and L into slots C, D, E, F, G, H, J, K, and L. Ends of front axle should be pushed through holes A and B.' " While marshalling the indicated parts in their proper order, I emphasized to my rapt listeners the necessity of patience and perseverance. "Haste makes waste, you know," I reminded them. "Rome wasn't built in a day. Remember, your daddy isn't always going to be here to show you."

"Where *are* you going to be?" they demanded.

"In the movies, if I can arrange it," I snarled. Poising tabs C, D, E, F, G, H, J, K, and L in one hand and the corresponding slots in the other, I essayed a union of the two, but in vain. The moment I made one set fast and tackled another, tab

228

and slot would part company, thumbing their noses at me. Although the children were too immature to understand, I saw in a flash where the trouble lay. Some idiotic employee at the factory had punched out the wrong design, probably out of sheer spite. So that was his game, eh? I set my lips in a grim line and, throwing one hundred and fifty-seven pounds of fighting fat into the effort, pounded the component parts into a homogeneous mass.

"There," I said with a gasp, "that's close enough. Now then, who wants candy? One, two, three—everybody off to the candy store!"

"We wanna finish the delivery truck!" they wailed. "Mummy, he won't let us finish the delivery truck!" Threats, cajolery, bribes were of no avail. In their jungle code, a twenty-nine-cent gewgaw bulked larger than a parent's love. Realizing that I was dealing with a pair of monomaniacs, I determined to show them who was master and wildly began locking the cardboard units helter-skelter, without any regard for the directions. When sections refused to fit, I gouged them with my nails and forced them together, cackling shrilly. The side panels collapsed;

with a bestial oath, I drove a safety pin through them and lashed them to the roof. I used paper clips, bobby pins, anything I could lay my hands on. My fingers fairly flew and my breath whistled in my throat. "You want a delivery truck, do you?" I panted. "All right, I'll show you!" As merciful blackness closed in, I was on my hands and knees, bunting the infernal thing along with my nose and whinnying, "Roll, confound you, roll!"

"Absolute quiet," a carefully modulated voice was saying, "and fifteen of the white tablets every four hours." I opened my eyes carefully in the darkened room. Dimly I picked out a knifelike character actor in a Vandyke beard and pencil-striped pants folding a stethoscope into his bag. "Yes," he added thoughtfully, "if we play our cards right, this ought to be a long, expensive recovery." From far away, I could hear my wife's voice bravely trying to control her anxiety.

"What if he becomes restless, Doctor?"

"Get him a detective story," returned the leech. "Or better still, a nice, soothing picture puzzle—something he can do with his hands."

230

THE LONGER THE LIP,
THE SMOOTHER THE GRIFT

Do young men nowadays still become hope-
lessly enamored of married women easily ten years
their senior who have mocking, humorous mouths,
eyes filled with tender raillery, and indulgent
husbands? Back in the twenties, when it was a
lot easier for a woman to be ten years my senior
than it is now, I was privileged to know one who
fitted these specifications and who inflamed me
deeply. By the time the lava cooled, I found that
the tender raillery in her eyes was actually pseu-
doblepsis, a form of myopia, and that her husband
was somewhat less indulgent than I had supposed.
The experience, nevertheless, had a certain salutary
effect. It forever dispelled the notion I had cher-

ished from boyhood that a mustache makes you irresistible to the opposite sex.

I grew one that summer in a dogged attempt to bridge the disparity in our ages, modelling it on those worn by the Coldstream Guards I remembered in the pages of *Chatterbox*. It was a dismal tuft—cinnamon-colored, rather spiky, inclined to droop at the corners in a depressing Mongol fashion. If I resembled anybody, which was questionable, it was Ginger Dick or Russet in W. W. Jacobs' stories. After carefully grooming and disbudding it for three weeks, I entered the lady's presence in snowy flannels, negligently plucking a round-bellied mandolin. There was no immediate reaction. At length I yawned, flicked an infinitesimal speck of zweiback from my lapel, and inquired lightly, "Notice anything different?" "God, yes," she replied in a strangled voice. "You look like a dentist. A mechanical dentist," she added cruelly, bursting into a shriek of maniacal laughter. I arose, my lip curling as far as the mustache would permit, and, stumbling over a rubber plant, swept out of her life.

I bare this early scar only to prove that my credentials are in order at a moment when mustaches, for some inexplicable reason, suddenly seem to have become especially newsworthy. As influential and responsible a journal as the New York *Post*, for instance, apparently considers them significant enough to merit a poll of opinion. A few days ago it sent its inquiring photographer out to ask five mustached citizens at random, "Is a mustache an advantage or a disadvantage to you in the business world?" Every man interviewed replied without equivocation that a mustache had aided him immeasurably in his career. All concurred that it gave them a "more mature and distinguished appearance" and inspired "confidence." One of them, a stock clerk, stated, "I am 21, and I find that the mustache makes people think I am much older, and they seem to have more confidence in me." Another, a salesman who claimed that he was known to the business world as "Lester with the Mustache," said, "A mustache seems to give the customer confidence that he is dealing with a person who knows his business."

Now, gracious knows I approve wholeheartedly of anything that tends to banish distrust and engender a universal spirit of faith, but I doubt that a few hundred hairs on the upper lip, no matter how silky, can supplant a triple-A rating in Bradstreet. The most reassuring mustaches I ever saw were those worn by automobile salesmen around Hollywood, a notoriously factitious crew. These foxy-nosed brethren all had rich mahogany sun tans, luxuriant mustaches stiff with pomade, and prematurely white wavy hair. Max Beerbohm once observed that men with prematurely white hair are invariably charlatans. The average Hollywood foxy-nose was acutely aware of this (he was, needless to say, a constant reader of Beerbohm), and he sought to offset it by camouflaging himself with a solid, executive mustache. He fooled nobody —nobody, that is, except me.

How the particular one I recall ever tracked me to the dispiriting hacienda where I lay brooding I cannot imagine; it was the least prepossessing in a weedy suburb full of raw-food addicts, astrologers, and obscure fire worshippers. I found him smirking on the doorstep one dank forenoon as I was reaching for my morning avocado. He wore a rough shooting coat of hyper-tweed and woven

234

wire, a primrose-yellow muffler tied Ascot fashion, brogues that had been perforated until they were simply scraps of leather, and a silver signet ring weighing just under four pounds. The twin points of his mustache were needle-sharp and he exhaled a scent of fabulously expensive cologne.

"Howdy, Aguinaldo," he saluted, clapping me familiarly on the back. "The lady of the house in?"

"I'm the lady of the house," I said coldly, sacrificing accuracy for hauteur. Before I could raise the drawbridge, he slid past me into the living room and zipped open his briefcase, his eyes taking rapid inventory of the furnishings.

"Gloomy little hole you've got here," he commented. "What do you do, store roots in it?"

"That's for me to know and you to find out," I parried. He pretended not to have heard my riposte and drew forth a limp leather manual.

"Now, here's the way it figures, Mac," he began. "The best we can do for you on a new Moosup convertible is fourteen hundred skins."

"Hey, wait a minute!" I protested. "I never—"

"Quiet!" he ordered. "I'll do the talking around

235

here. Now, judging from this layout"—he looked about critically—"you want to buy the car on time. Suppose you let us have twelve hundred down—"

I interrupted and, mincing no words, made it clear I already owned a car that he could see on his departure, which I hoped was imminent.

"You mean that stem-winder in the driveway?" he sneered. "That's not a car—that's transportation!"

The cheap gibe at my little bluebell stung my cheeks to flame.

"It's good enough for me," I blazed, "and anyway, I'd drive a—a brewery wagon if it got me there!"

"Where?" he asked.

"Where—wherever I was going," I replied weakly.

"Where *are* you going—to a dog fight?" He chuckled. "You certainly have the clothes for it." I suddenly realized I no longer held trump cards and laid my hand authoritatively on his coat collar. He brushed it aside without rancor.

"Look, friend," he purred, "you've got me

236

wrong. Hatcher & Gonsdorf don't sell automobiles—we sell *good will*."

"You do?" I asked, struck by this profound merchandising philosophy.

"Of course," he said. "Do you think I'd sacrifice flesh and blood for a lousy commission? I'd rather have your friendship." His honest emotion shamed me; I saw I had done him a deep injustice.

"That hits me where I live, fellow," I said shyly. We shook hands.

"They don't come any whiter than you, old man," he said, his voice husky. "Now, get your coat. I want to see you behind the wheel of a job I've got outside. Test its fingertip control, self-annealing shock absorbers, and forty-seven big new features. I don't want you to buy it. As a matter of fact, it's not for sale."

It was either the man's hypnotic mustache or some drug like scopolamine he introduced into my coffee; anyway, on the dot of noon I issued dreamily from the Friendly Finance Company with an empty poke in one hand and the title to a new juggernaut in the other. My chest swelled with pride as I paused on the curb and surveyed its sleek black body edged with glistening chromework, its virginal white-wall tires. Then, settling my cap like Barney Oldfield's, I crawled in and pointed the nose of the machine toward the open road. Motorists and pedestrians alike bit their lips in envy as I streaked past, annihilating time and space with a casual pressure of the foot. At a traffic light I overheard two old ladies in a battered blue sedan discussing me in awed whispers. "That's Luis Escobar, the South American matinée idol," murmured one. "They say he commands upward of ninety thousand reals a picture. A woman isn't safe with a man like that." I lounged back, my eyes heavy-lidded with boredom, and contemplated trips to Baja California, the Everglades, the Gaspé Peninsula. I might even have Buckminster Fuller design me a Dymaxion trailer, embodying certain innovations I had projected for a long time . . .

Five miles from the Friendly Finance Company, a horrid temblor shook the motor. Some instinctive mechanical bent warned me to pull into the nearest gas station. I had barely drawn up before a mosque-shaped lubritorium when the car emitted a deep, phthisic cough. Almost simultaneously, a Marmon engine of the vintage of 1928, covered with barnacles, dropped out of the hood and lay steaming between the front wheels. Two minutes later, an incredibly handsome young man, whose prematurely white hair proclaimed him a rare mixture of charlatan and chump, crept out of the driver's seat, borrowed a nickel from the attendant, and rode home on the streetcar. He's still looking for a certain auto salesman, formerly in the employ of Hatcher & Gonsdorf— chap with a dashing black mustache. As I get the story, he wants to pull it out by the roots.

IF AN IN-LAW
MEET AN OUTLAW

I was stretched out soaking blissfully in the tub this morning—well, not actually stretched out; more crouched in an old wash boiler with the janitor turning a watering can over me—when I was suddenly suffused with a sense of the utmost well-being, as though someone had just presented me with a billion tax-free dollars. I sprang out of the boiler, wrapped myself in a fleecy Circassian girl who happened to be hanging there, and leafed rapidly through my mail. Outside of a terse note from the public library reporting that my request for a card had been approved, and three swatches of tweed from a Hollywood tailor, there seemed to be no grounds for elation. On the contrary, the mound of bills and summonses clearly indicated

241

the bailiffs were on my tail and determined to clap
me into Marshalsea Prison for debt. After scratching about a while, however, I managed to reconstruct my train of thought. It was simple enough.
It had merely occurred to me that though my
youth is rapidly receding into the distance, old
age has one sweet consolation in store. There are
going to be fewer and fewer of those family get-
togethers over the holidays.

Why anybody in his right mind doesn't hop
into bed like Turkey Gehrke the day before
Thanksgiving and stay there until the relatives
clear is beyond me. From Halloween to the Ides
of March, the average American home is constantly filled with a succession of heavy, overfed
uncles dozing on lounges, their uneasy slumber
punctuated now and again by a voluptuous belch.
The next time you take the only girl in the world
in your arms and look into those violet pools, remember one thing. You're simply a peg on which
she hopes to hang a series of family dinners. You
may think you're Galahad, or Monsieur Beau-
caire, or Henry Kaiser, but you're not. You're
only a caterer.

242

Where the relatives come from, once the banns are posted, from under what stones, it is impossible to say. Personally, I jilted hundreds of deucedly attractive girls solely because of their folks. In my search for a helpmeet, I interviewed scores of applicants from every clime: buxom, taffy-haired wenches from Copenhagen, sloe-eyed Eurasians from the Bubbling Well Road, saucy midinettes from the Rue de Rivoli, cool Devonshire beauties with skin like clotted cream, and placid, deep-bosomed wildflowers from the Kirghiz Steppe. In every case the candidate had family somewhere in the background, crouched ready to make my life a hell. At length I met a tall and lovely dryad from the Lone Star State, imperious yet tender, innocent but incredibly versed in womanly wiles. Damn my eyes, sir, she was as pretty as a peony. I loved her for herself alone, but I took the precaution of looking her up in Dun and Bradstreet. Her people had left her four hundred thousand acres in the Panhandle, a controlling interest in United States Steel, and a twin-Diesel yacht sleeping twelve. Every hour, on the hour, three men ran in with bushel baskets and emptied a flood of gold eagles around her feet. She swore she had no kin; I had lawyers trace her lineage back to Frederick Barbarossa until they confirmed it. The day of our wedding dawned on schedule. As we mounted the steps of St. Thomas', her eyes streaming with gratitude at having won such a prize, a gnarled old desert rat touched his forelock. She acknowledged the greeting absently.

"Who's that?" I demanded, recoiling.

"My uncle," she replied. "He's a sheepherder from Canberra. He's coming to dinner tomorrow night." I bent over on the pretext of tying my bootlace, squirmed adroitly through a policeman's legs, and in forty-eight hours was paddling up the St. Lawrence under an assumed name.

For all my vigilance, nevertheless, retribution overtook me at last. When I finally struck the colors to the breathtaking creature who shares my joint account, I was satisfied she was an orphan. Her one living tie was a rheumatic King Charles spaniel, and even then I persuaded it to sign a paper releasing me from any obligation. At my insistence, we were married in the dead of night on an islet off Casco Bay; I instantly cut down the parson and witnesses, left a cairn to mark their

244

lonely grave, and headed back to the mainland. Only the stars knew our secret, I exulted to myself.

And then, within the week, her relatives started filing forward. Puling babes and graybeard loons sprang from our carpet as from a seedbed. Jail doors yawned to disgorge maternal uncles; elderly harpies in bombazine, bearing rubber plants, trooped through the bathroom deriding our linens. Pimply nephews awoke me at eight in the morning to put the sleeve on me for a small loan.

The average man would have lost his head, screamed and threatened divorce; not so I. I gently took my wife's windpipe between the forefinger and thumb of the left hand and massaged it until she agreed that no relative would ever again cross the threshold. The device worked for a while, but gradually she undermined me. More and more faces began appearing at the holiday board; today it looks like the Congress of Vienna. Every Christmas I pay off on a hundred and thirty-two turkeys and all I ever get is a drumstick. That's wedlock, brother.

Last Thanksgiving, for instance, I was curled

up peacefully like a shrimp, mouth ajar and half-way through a thrilling dream in which Jane Russell had stopped at my mountain lodge to dry her things. Just as she had retired behind the screen and I was purling, "Why, little girl, I'm old enough to be your father," the doorbell wrenched me from my fantasy. I landed convulsively on the bedroom floor, flailing at the air. The *signora* finished applying make-up to lips already like coral, and rose from her dressing table.

"Welcome back, sweet," she snapped. "Dust a bit of talc on that beard and greet our guests. They've been here over an hour."

As I scrambled into my clothes, I could hear the jackals in the living room opening my last bottle of liqueur Scotch and discussing me freely.

"He'll never amount to a damn," stated a brother-in-law who had quit work during the Harding Administration. "It's the kids I'm sorry for."

"Did you see that mark under her eye?" whispered a niece. "He threw a cottage pudding at her in a fit of temper."

"I met him coming out of a pawnshop Tuesday,"

related another. "He had his arm around a platinum blonde."

They had finished the Scotch and were opening the cooking sherry when I entered. The premises were filled with steam and a sickening smell of giblets. Besides the usual covetous faces, there were several unfamiliar ones—a Free French sailor who mistakenly supposed himself at a radio broadcast and an aged beldame with an ear trumpet who kept asking querulously for the next train to Cynwyd.

Over the hubbub, from the kitchen, floated madame's voice offering to triple the maid's salary if she would stay through dinner. Selecting one of the less revolting young cousins, I sat down by him and attempted to draw him into conversation.

"Well, what kept you out of the Army, Mac?" I inquired genially. "You're a big strong hulk."

With a boorishness typical of the entire clan, he stalked off, obviously flustered by my question. By now, the company had divided roughly into two groups—the older matrons dissecting my wife's clothes and their menfolk predicting my impending bankruptcy. At three o'clock, when the dinner

247

bell sounded, the room was revolving about me like a carousel. By the time I fought my way to the table, the turkey had dwindled to a pathetic little pile of bones. I tamped down a glutinous amalgam of sweet potatoes and marshmallows, and retired to the drawing room to chink up the crannies with English walnuts. The room was empty, save for a nephew sprawled on the floor tearing random pages out of my first editions and a stray grandfather with snuff on his lapel.

"Hello, sonny," he quavered. "Who be you— friend of the family?" I grunted noncommittally and tried extracting what nourishment I could from a strip of preserved orange peel. The old gaffer peered furtively over his shoulder, leaned closer to me. "You look like a nice, clean-cut young feller," he observed, "so I'll give you some advice. Don't never sign a note for the bozo that lives here."

"I happen to be the bozo," I snarled, rising with awful majesty.

"Yes, I know," he said hurriedly, "but I'm just warnin' you. He's a crook; he'd steal your eye-teeth. Any time you see a man with them little pig

248

eyes——" I burst my bonds spang in the middle of my character analysis and finished the evening under a table in a neighborhood tavern. It was drafty and I got sawdust in my ears, but at least the cat I met there had no grudge against me. He wasn't even a second cousin by marriage.

SEND NO MONEY,
HONEY

I HAVE a well-defined suspicion, bounded on the south by Fortieth Street and the north by Fifty-seventh, that anybody venturing into the Times Square area who was not already sick of phosphorescent carnations is, by now, sick of phosphorescent carnations. Exactly when the craze for these luminous hybrids captured the popular imagination is uncertain—possibly during the dimout. At any rate, since then every midtown cranny too small for a watchmaker, a popcorn machine, or a publisher's remainders boasts its own little altar of black velvet from which carnations and brooches of debatable value give off a spectral greenish glow. It is not altogether clear, incident-

251

ally, whether people buy them to wear or to worship in private. The only time I believe I ever saw one off the leash was at the Rialto Theatre, when a woman's head, radiating a distinct nimbus, rose in a grisly, disembodied fashion and floated past me up the aisle. I assume it was illuminated from below by a phosphorescent corsage, but it may merely have been an ordinary disembodied head viewing the feature at a reduced rate of admission.

The vogue could be discounted as a sheerly local phenomenon except that a short time ago a prominent jobber of glowing novelties decided to invade the mail-order field. Hiring the back cover of a breezy magazine called *Laff*, the Glow-in-the-Dark Necktie Company of Chicago exhibited a twinkling four-in-hand flashing the words "WILL YOU KISS ME IN THE DARK, BABY?," accompanied by this text:

Girls Can't Resist this KISS ME NECKTIE as it GLOWS in the Dark! By Day a Lovely Swank Tie . . . By Night a Call to Love in Glowing Words! . . . Here's the most amazing spectacular necktie that you ever wore, a smart, wrinkleproof, tailored cravat, which at night is a thrilling sensation! It's smart, superb class by day, and just imagine in the dark it seems like a necktie of compelling allure, sheer magic! Like a miracle of light there comes a pulsing, glowing question—WILL YOU KISS ME IN THE DARK, BABY? Think of the surprise, the awe you will cause! There's no trick, no hid-

252

den batteries, no switches or foolish horseplay, but a thing of beauty as the question emerges gradually to life, touched by the wand of darkness, and your girl will gasp with wonder as it takes form so amazingly. . . . Send no money, here's all you do . . .

However unpredictable its reception by the beau monde, there is no gainsaying the romantic appeal of the glowing necktie in terms of theatre. Before some energetic dramatist weaves the idea into a smash operetta or Leon Leonidoff preëmpts it for one of his opulent Music Hall presentations, I hasten to stake out my claim with the following playlet. If Metro-Goldwyn-Mayer would like it as a vehicle for Greer Garson (and I'm ready to throw in a whiffle-tree and two wheels), I shall be wearing a corned-beef sandwich this evening in the third booth at the Brass Rail. Just walk by rapidly and drop the three dollars on the floor.

[Scene: *The conservatory of the country club at Heublein's Fens, Ohio. Fern Replevin, an utterly lovely creature of twenty-four whose mouth wanders at will over her features in the manner of Greer Garson's, sits lost in dreams, watching a cirrus formation in the moonlit sky. Offstage the usual Saturday-night dance is in progress, and as*

253

mingled laughter and music drift in to Fern, she softly hums the air the orchestra is playing, "If Love Should Call."]

FERN:

If love should call, and you were I,
And I were you, and love should call,
How happy I could be with I,
And you with you, if love should call.
Your shoulders broad, your instep arched,
Without your kiss my lips are parched.
For love comes late, and now, and soon,
At midnight's crack and blazing noon.
My arms are ready, the wine is heady,
If love should call.

(Lafcadio Replevin, Fern's father, enters. He belongs to the Vigorous and Tweedy school—is headmaster, in fact—is leader in his community and a man who knows his way around the block, if no further. He has, as the saying goes, a groatsworth of wit in a guinea-sized noddle. Maybe the saying doesn't go just this way, but it certainly describes Lafcadio.)

LAFCADIO: Oh, there you are, daughter; I've been looking all over for you. Why aren't you inside dancing with your fiancé, Fleetwood Rumsey, that is by far the richest man in town and owner of

254

feed mills galore throughout the vicinity? There hasn't been any tiffin' between you, has there?

FERN (*indicating some scones and tea on the table*): Only what you see on this tray.

LAFCADIO: Then why are you staring at those clouds so pensively?

FERN: Perhaps I'm more cirrus-minded than the other girls.

LAFCADIO: Well, I don't like to see you moon around. As for me, I'm going in and have a drink with that new librarian. She's as thin as a *lath* and pretty *stucco* on herself, but I guess we can get *plastered*. (*He exits chuckling. Sunk in reverie, Fern is unaware that a man has emerged from behind a rubber plant and is regarding her narrowly. Rex Beeswanger is thirty-odd, a thoroughbred from his saturnine eyebrow to the tip of his well-polished shoe. His clothes, which he wears with casual elegance, bear an unmistakable metropolitan stamp. He is shod by Thom McAn, gloved by Fownes, belted by Hickok, and cravatted by Glow-in-Dark.*)

REX (*softly*): If you don't love him, why go through with it?

255

FERN (*whirling*): Oh! You startled me.

REX: Did I?

FERN: Did you what?

REX: Startle you.

FERN: Yes. I mean I was sunk in a reverie, and you spoke to me suddenly, and that startled me.

REX: You see things clearly, don't you? You're a very direct person.

FERN: Am I?

REX: Are you what?

FERN: A very direct person.

REX: Yes. When I startled you out of the reverie in which you were sunk, you didn't pretend I hadn't. That would have been cheap. And you're not cheap.

FERN: What are we talking about?

REX: Does it matter? Does anything matter but silver slanting rain on the cruel lilacs and compassion in the heart's deep core?

FERN: Who are you? You haven't even told me your name.

REX: Just a bird of passage. Call me Rex Beeswanger if you like.

FERN (*savoring it*): Rex Beeswanger. I've always wanted to know someone named Rex Bees-wanger. It's—it's instinct with springtime and the song of larks.

Rex: May I kiss you?

Fern: Oh, Rex, you've got to give me time to think. We've know each other less than forty-eight hours.

Rex (*fiercely*): Is that all love means to you— narrow little conventions, smug barriers holding two kinsprits apart? I thought you finer than that.

Fern: Yes, but there's so much light in here. It's like a cafeteria or something. (*For answer, Rex extinguishes the lamp. Instantly the legend "WILL YOU KISS ME IN THE DARK, BABY?" springs into relief on his tie. The music inside swells and, silhouetted against the window, Fern lifts her voice in vibrant melody.*)

Fern:

> You glowed in the dark, I saw your spark,
> You left your mark on me.
> You're wrinkleproof, and so aloof,
> You made a goof of me.
> I might have been coy with another boy,
> But not when you said "Ahoy" to me.
> I'm a pearl of a girl, so give me a whirl.
> Ah, don't be a perfect churl to me.

(As Fern and Rex lock lips, harsh light floods the room, and Fleetwood Rumsey, his bull neck distended with rage, stands glaring balefully at the pair.)

FLEETWOOD: So this is what gives out behind my back.

FERN *(returning his ring)*: Fleetwood, I think there is something you ought to know.

FLEETWOOD: In due time. First, I mean to show this meddling upstart how we deal with kiss thieves in Heublein's Fens. *(Sidestepping nimbly, Rex pins him in a grip of steel and slowly forces him to his knees.)*

REX: *Les jeux sont faits,* "Short Weight" Rumsey!

FLEETWOOD *(paling)*: You—you know me then?

REX: Your leering visage adorns every rogue's gallery in the country. *(Encircling his captive's wrists with a set of shiny handcuffs)* Thanks to you, Miss Replevin, a notorious malefactor has received his just lumps. He had been adulterating his poultry mash with sawdust and sub-specifica-

258

tion brans, causing a serious crimp in egg production.

FERN: My woman's intuition warned me. I wouldn't wipe my feet on the best part of him.

REX: Governmental appreciation will follow in due course. We have every reason to believe him the agent of a foreign power.

FLEETWOOD (*gutturally*): I get efen wiz you for zis zome time, Mr. Rex Beeswanger!

REX: Take him away, boys. (*Fleetwood is removed by two burly operatives as a corps de ballet of forty trained dancers swirls about Fern and Rex, symbolizing the gratitude of local poultrymen and 4-H Clubs alike. As the spectacle reaches a climax, the ushers, equipped with phosphorescent truncheons, flit through the darkened theatre like myriad fireflies and awaken the audience. On second thought, I don't believe I'll be in the Brass Rail tonight after all. There's no sense sticking my chin out.*)

CURTAIN